Science and Technology Concepts for Middle Schools™

Organisms—From Macro to Micro

**Student
Guide
and
Source
Book**

NATIONAL SCIENCE RESOURCES CENTER

The National Science Resources Center (NSRC) is operated by the Smithsonian Institution and the National Academies to improve the teaching of science in the nation's schools. The NSRC disseminates information about exemplary teaching resources, develops curriculum materials, and conducts outreach programs of leadership development and technical assistance to help school districts implement inquiry-centered science programs.

SMITHSONIAN INSTITUTION

The Smithsonian Institution was created by act of Congress in 1846 "for the increase and diffusion of knowledge. . . ." This independent federal establishment is the world's largest museum complex and is responsible for public and scholarly activities, exhibitions, and research projects nationwide and overseas. Among the objectives of the Smithsonian is the application of its unique resources to enhance elementary and secondary education.

THE NATIONAL ACADEMIES

The National Academies are nonprofit organizations that provide independent advice to the nation on matters of science, technology, and medicine. The National Academies consist of four organizations: the National Academy of Sciences, the National Academy of Engineering, the Institute of Medicine, and the National Research Council. The National Academy of Sciences was created in 1863 by a congressional charter. Under this charter, the National Research Council was established in 1916, the National Academy of Engineering in 1964, and the Institute of Medicine in 1970.

STC/MS PROJECT SPONSORS

National Science Foundation
Bristol-Myers Squibb Foundation
Dow Chemical Company
DuPont Company
Hewlett-Packard Company
The Robert Wood Johnson Foundation
Carolina Biological Supply Company

Science and Technology Concepts for Middle Schools™

Organisms—From Macro to Micro

Student Guide and Source Book

 National Science Resources Center

THE NATIONAL ACADEMIES Smithsonian Institution

Published by Carolina Biological Supply Company
Burlington, North Carolina

NOTICE This material is based upon work supported by the National Science Foundation under Grant No. ESI-9618091. Any opinions, findings, and conclusions or recommendations expressed in this material are those of the authors and do not necessarily reflect views of the National Science Foundation, the Smithsonian Institution, or the National Academies.

This project was supported, in part,
by the
National Science Foundation
Opinions expressed are those of the authors
and not necessarily those of the Foundation

ISBN 978-0-89278-924-5

Published by Carolina Biological Supply Company, 2700 York Road, Burlington, NC 27215. Call toll free 1-800-334-5551.

Cover design and illustration by Max-Karl Winkler; cover photo Lake Reflections, Kenai Peninsula, Alaska, © Ron Niebrugge/www.WildNatureImages.com.
Printed in the United States of America

CB787911004
♻ Printed on recycled paper.

Organisms—From Macro to Micro

MODULE DEVELOPMENT STAFF

Developer/Writer
Henry Milne

Science Advisor
Robert Matthews
Department of Entomology,
University of Georgia

Editor
Lorraine Coffey

Contributing Writers
Catherine Stephens
Daniel Doersch

Illustrator
Taina Litwak

Photographic Research
Christine Hauser
Maggie Sliker

STC/MS PROJECT STAFF

Principal Investigator
Sally Goetz Shuler, Executive Director, NSRC

Project Director
Kitty Lou Smith

Curriculum Developers
David Marsland
Henry Milne
Carol O'Donnell
Dane Toler

Publications Director
Heather Dittbrenner

Managing Editors
Linda Griffin Kean
Dorothy Sawicki

Illustration Coordinator
Max-Karl Winkler

Photo Editor
Christine Hauser

Graphic Designer
Heidi M. Kupke

Researcher/Writer
Carolyn Hanson

Reader Editor
Linda Harteker

DESIGN CONSULTATION
Isely &/or Clark Design

STC/MS Project Advisors for *Organisms—From Macro to Micro*

George Andrykovitch, Associate Professor of Biology, George Mason University

D. Wayne Coats, Zoologist, Environmental Research Center, Smithsonian Institution

Daniel Doersch, Teacher, Green Bay Area Public School District, Wisconsin

Patricia Gossel, Curator, National Museum of American History

LeLeng Isaacs, Professor, Department of Biological Sciences, Goucher College

Jennifer Kuzma, Staff Officer, The National Academies, Board on Biology

Craig Laufer, Professor, Department of Biology, Hood College

Lynn Lewis, Associate Professor, Mary Washington College

Robert Matthews, Professor, Department of Entomology, University of Georgia

Wanda Rinker, Teacher, West Windsor/Plainsboro School District, New Jersey

Patricia Shields, Course Coordinator, Introductory Biology, George Mason University

Eileen Smith, Teacher, Montgomery County, Maryland, Public Schools

Kay Stieger, Teacher, Montgomery County, Maryland, Public Schools

Paul Williams, Emeritus Professor, University of Wisconsin—Madison, Wisconsin Fast Plants™ Program

Foreword

Community leaders and state and local school officials across the country are recognizing the need to implement science education programs consistent with the National Science Education Standards as we strive to attain the important national goal of scientific literacy for all students in the 21st century. The Standards present a bold vision of science education. They identify what students at various levels should know and be able to do. They also emphasize the importance of transforming the science curriculum in a way that encourages students to engage actively in scientific inquiry—thereby developing conceptual understanding as well as problem-solving skills.

We believe that the development of effective, standards-based, inquiry-centered curriculum materials is a key step in achieving scientific literacy. The National Science Resources Center (NSRC) has responded to this challenge through the Science and Technology Concepts for Middle Schools (STC/MS) program. With the publication of the STC/MS modules, schools now have a rich set of curriculum resources for middle school students that embody scientific inquiry and hands-on learning.

Since its founding in 1985, the NSRC has made many contributions to the goal of achieving scientific literacy for all students. In addition to developing the Science and Technology for Children (STC) program—an inquiry-centered science curriculum for grades K through 6—the NSRC has been active in disseminating information on science teaching resources, in preparing school district leaders to spearhead science education reform, and in providing technical assistance to school districts. These programs have had an important impact on science education throughout the country.

The transformation of science education is a challenging task that will continue to require the kind of strategic thinking and insistence on excellence that the NSRC has demonstrated in all of its curriculum development and outreach programs. Its sponsoring organizations, the Smithsonian Institution and the National Academies, take great pride in the publication of this exciting new science program for middle schools.

J. DENNIS O'CONNOR
Former Under Secretary for Science
Smithsonian Institution

BRUCE M. ALBERTS
President
National Academy of Sciences

Preface

The National Science Resources Center's (NSRC) mission is to improve the learning and teaching of science for K-12 students. As an organization of two prestigious scientific institutions—the National Academies and the Smithsonian Institution—the NSRC is dedicated to the establishment of effective science programs for all students. To contribute to that goal, the NSRC has developed and published two comprehensive, research-based science curriculum programs: the Science and Technology for Children® (STC®) program for students in grades K-6, and the Science and Technology Concepts for Middle Schools™ (STC/MS™) program for students in grades 6-8.

The STC/MS curriculum project was launched in 1997. The overall design of the instructional materials and the process by which they were developed are based on a foundation of research. The STC/MS courses were informed by research on cognitive development, teaching, learning, assessment, and the culture of schools.

The STC/MS curriculum materials consist of eight courses. Through these courses, students build an understanding of important concepts in life, earth, and physical sciences and in technology; learn critical-thinking skills; and develop positive attitudes toward science and technology. The STC/MS program materials are designed to meet the challenge of the National Science Education Standards to place scientific inquiry at the core of science education programs. Specifically, the National Science Education Standards state that "...students in grades 5–8 should be provided opportunities to engage in full and partial inquiries.... With an appropriate curriculum and adequate instruction, middle school students can develop the skills of investigation and the understanding that scientific inquiry is guided by knowledge, observations, ideas, and questions." STC/MS also addresses the national technology standards published by the International Technology Education Association.

Informed by research and guided by standards, the design of the STC/MS courses addresses four critical goals:

- Use of effective student and teacher assessment strategies to improve learning and teaching.
- Integration of literacy into the learning of science by giving students the lens of language to focus and clarify their thinking and activities.
- Enhanced learning using new technologies to help students visualize processes and relationships that are normally invisible or difficult to understand.
- Incorporation of strategies to actively engage parents to support the learning process.

The research and development process has included trial teaching and field-testing nationwide with geographically and ethnically diverse student populations, as well as the active involvement of the scientific and engineering communities. This process has ensured that the learning experiences contained in each module reflect current scientific thinking, and are pedagogically sound and developmentally appropriate for students.

The NSRC is grateful to the Smithsonian Institution and the National Academies for their overall project support and for sharing their scientific expertise—critical for the development of world-class products. Support for project staff and the associated work to produce and publish these materials has been made possible by the National Science Foundation, our publisher Carolina Biological Supply Company, and numerous private foundations and corporations, including Bristol-Myers Squibb Foundation, The Dow Chemical Company Foundation, DuPont, the Hewlett-Packard Company, and The Robert Wood Johnson Foundation.

The NSRC would like to acknowledge Douglas M. Lapp, former NSRC Executive Director, for his vision and leadership on the STC/MS project. The STC/MS development staff, under the direction of Kitty Lou Smith, and the publications staff, under the direction of Heather Dittbrenner, working in cooperation with Dorothy Sawicki, Managing Editor for the first four modules, and Linda Griffin Kean, Managing Editor for the second four modules, are to be commended for their creativity, dedication, and commitment to develop these excellent curriculum materials that will be used to improve the learning and teaching of middle school science in the nation's schools.

We welcome comments from students and teachers about their experiences with the STC/MS program materials and recommendations for ways the STC/MS courses can be improved.*

Sally Goetz Shuler
Executive Director
National Science Resources Center

*Please forward your feedback and suggestions to STC/MS Program, National Science Resources Center, Smithsonian Institution, Washington, DC 20560-0403.

Acknowledgments

The author expresses his appreciation for the support of STC/MS colleagues Kitty Lou Smith, David Marsland, Carol O'Donnell, Dane Toler, Matt Bailey, and Carolyn Hanson throughout the conceptualization, preparation, trial teaching, field-testing, and commercial preparation of *Organisms—From Macro to Micro*. Special thanks go out to Dr. Robert Matthews and Dr. Paul Williams for serving as technical reviewers. Special thanks also goes out to field-test teachers Daniel Doersch, Angie Ruzicka, Scott Baker, and Eileen Smith for their continuing support throughout the development of the commercial edition of the module.

The National Science Resources Center thanks the following individuals who contributed to the development of *Organisms—From Macro to Micro*:

John W. Cross, author of popular educational Web sites hosted by the Missouri Botanical Garden

Charles Drewes, Professor of Invertebrate Zoology, Neurobiology, and Bioethics, Iowa State University, Ames, Iowa

Dan Lauffer, Program Manager, Wisconsin Fast Plants™ Program, University of Wisconsin—Madison

Coe Williams, Program Coordinator, Wisconsin Fast Plants™ Program, University of Wisconsin—Madison

Patricia A. Hagan, Senior Associate, The McKenzie Group, Washington, D.C.

Jonathan Jones, Principal (retired), Cabin John Middle School, Potomac, Maryland

Robert Domergue, Principal, Robert Frost Middle School, Rockville, Maryland

The NSRC gratefully acknowledges the following individuals and school systems for their assistance with the national field-testing of *Organisms—From Macro to Micro*:

The Einstein Project, Green Bay, Wisconsin
Site Coordinator: Sue Theno, Director, The Einstein Project

Green Bay Area Public School District, Green Bay, Wisconsin
Daniel Doersch, Teacher, Seymour Middle School
Cindy Wallendal, Teacher, Lombardi Middle School
Mary Conard, Teacher, DePere Middle School

Montgomery County Public Schools, Montgomery County, Maryland
Eileen Smith, Teacher, Robert Frost Middle School

Eugene Public School District, Eugene, Oregon
Site Coordinator: Bob Curtis, Science Specialist, Lane Educational Service District, Eugene, Oregon
Angie Ruzicka, Teacher, Cal Young Middle School
Scott Baker, Teacher, Cal Young Middle School
Courtney Abbott, Teacher, Kelly Middle School

West Windsor-Plainsboro Regional School District, West Windsor/Plainsboro, New Jersey

Site Coordinator: Miriam A. Robin, Supervisor of Science, Grades 6-8, Community Middle School

Kevin MacKenzie, Teacher, Community Middle School

Shereen Rochford, Teacher, Grover Middle School

Wanda Rinker, Teacher, Community Middle School

Huntsville School District, Huntsville, Alabama

Site Coordinator: Sandy Enger, University of Alabama, Huntsville, Alabama

Rhonda Hudson, Teacher, Eva School

Jennifer Elam, Teacher, Meridianville Middle School

Cheryl Adams, Teacher, Liberty Middle School

North Carolina, Alamance-Burlington School System

Mary Young, Teacher, Western Middle School

The NSRC also thanks the following individuals from Carolina Biological Supply Company for their contribution to the development of this module—

Dianne Gerlach, Director of Product Development

Bobby Mize, Department Head, Publications

Erin Krellwitz, Product Developer

Jennifer Manske, Publications Manager

Gary Metheny, Editor

Richard Franks, Director of Curriculum Marketing

Cindy Morgan, Senior Product Manager, Curriculum Marketing

Finally, the NSRC appreciates the contribution of its STC/MS project evaluation consultants:

Program Evaluation Research Group (PERG), Lesley College

Sabra Lee, Researcher, PERG

Center for the Study of Testing, Evaluation, and Education Policy (CSTEEP), Boston College

Joseph Pedulla, Director, CSTEEP

Contents

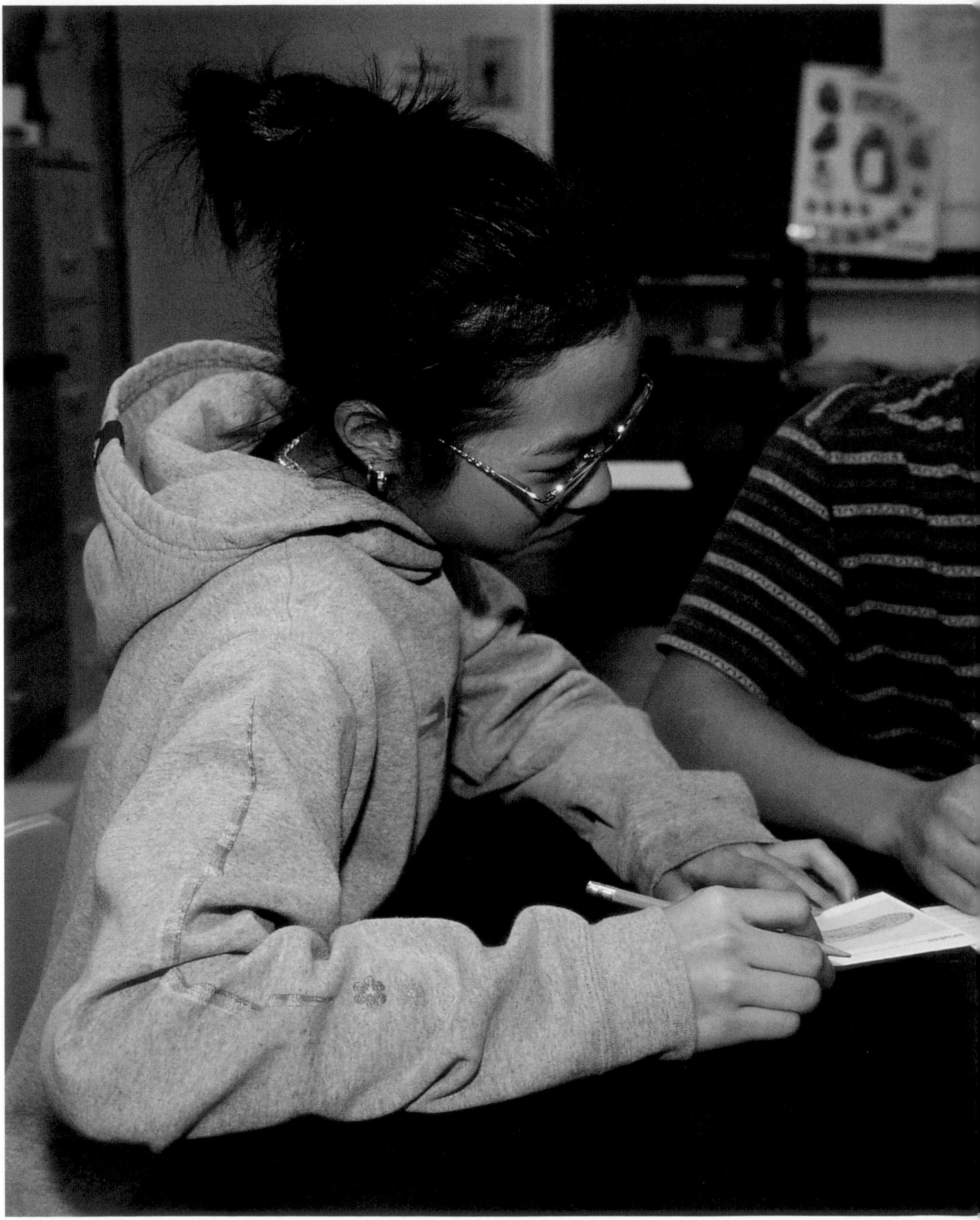

ERIC LONG, SMITHSONIAN INSTITUTION

PART 1 The Beginning

What Are Organisms?

Which organisms can you identify in this illustration?

INTRODUCTION

What are organisms? What makes them alive? What do they need in their environment to survive? How do they reproduce and pass along their characteristics to their offspring? How are they named and grouped by scientists for easy identification? These are just a few of many questions you will explore during this module. In this lesson, you will observe photos of some organisms that you'll examine in living detail later in the module. As you complete this introductory activity, think of questions about organisms that you would like to answer during this module.

OBJECTIVES FOR THIS LESSON

Develop a list of traits common to all living things.

Construct a working definition of the word "organism."

List some of the physical characteristics of the organisms shown on the organism photo cards.

Assign each organism a genus and species name.

Determine the appropriate place for each organism on the class habitat poster.

Getting Started

1. With your group, look over the organisms on the photo cards. Discuss the traits that these and all other living things have in common. Select at least five traits and list them in your science notebook.

2. Develop with your group a working definition of the word "organism," and write the definition in your science notebook. A working definition is one that changes as you discover more information.

3. Discuss your ideas with the class.

MATERIALS FOR LESSON 1

For your group
1 set of organism photo cards
1 copy of Student Sheet 1.1: Latin and Greek Terms
1 loose leaf ring
1 tag

ERIC LONG, SMITHSONIAN INSTITUTION

Students working with organism photo cards

Inquiry 1.1
Describing and Naming Organisms

PROCEDURE

1. Follow your teacher's directions for identifying the physical characteristics of each organism pictured on the organism photo cards.

2. With your class, read "What's in an Organism's Name?" at the end of this lesson.

3. Use Student Sheet 1.1: Latin and Greek Terms to assign each organism a logical scientific name, including both a genus and a species name. Print each name in the space provided on the inside of the organism card. Do not use both Latin and Greek words in the same name. You will learn the actual scientific names of these organisms as you work with them in greater detail in the module.

4. Work with your class to agree on the most suitable habitat for each organism, as seen in Figure 1.1. Be prepared to explain your choices.

Figure 1.1 *The class agrees that this organism would probably live in an aquatic habitat.*

Figure 1.2 *Keep the tag facing front for easy identification.*

5. Print your class period and your group members' names on the identification tag. Open the loose leaf ring. Insert the tag and the photo cards onto the ring and close it securely, as shown in Figure 1.2.

6. Return the tagged set of cards to your teacher for storage. Your teacher will give them back to you periodically to be revised.

REFLECTING ON WHAT YOU'VE DONE

1. On the basis of what you have learned in this lesson, work with your group to revise your list of traits common to all organisms and your working definition of organism as necessary. Record your revisions in your science notebook.

2. Discuss with your class the differences among a cougar, a mountain lion, and a puma, based on your homework research.

3. On the basis of what you've learned in this lesson, answer the following questions in your science notebook:

A. Why do scientists use Latin and Greek terms to create names for newly discovered organisms?

B. What do organisms need in their environment to be able to carry on their life processes and survive?

4. Write in your science notebooks three or more questions about organisms you would like to answer during this module. Be prepared to share one question with the class.

5. Visit the STC/MS™ Web site (http://www.stcms.si.edu) and browse some of the links listed for this module. If you have access to the Internet at home, consider sharing what you find with your family.

THAT'S LIFE!

In this lesson, you learned that an organism is a "living thing." That sounds pretty simple at first. When you start thinking about what it means to be "living," things get more complicated.

What makes living things different from nonliving things? All living things grow, reproduce, and eventually die. They all respond in some way to changes in their environment. And they all move. So growth, reproduction, response, and movement are referred to as "life processes."

Living or nonliving?

Among the life processes that living things share in common, movement might be the most surprising. People and other animals certainly move, but what about plants? You don't often see them walking down the street. In fact, plants do move, but their movements are usually less obvious than those of most animals. For example, plant leaves turn to face the sun, and roots grow and move toward a new water supply. But these movements occur so slowly that they are difficult to see without special photography.

Of course, there are several kinds of carnivorous, or meat-eating, plants whose movements are quite obvious. Try to convince the spider that gets trapped in the grip of a Venus flytrap that plants don't move!

Like the Venus flytrap, other living things need food. All living things take in nutrients

The Venus flytrap closes its leaves very quickly when the tiny trigger hairs on the inside surface are touched by the spider in a certain way.

DR. BARRY MEYERS-RICE, GALLERIA CARNIVORA

Despite their great difference in size, the elephant and the amoeba have much in common.

from their surroundings. Plants also use energy from the sun to manufacture their own food, in the form of glucose (or sugar), and then use that glucose as an energy source. Other organisms take in food and break it down into usable nutrients through the process called "digestion." Living things also take in oxygen and use it to break down nutrients for energy in a process called "cellular respiration."

While performing these life processes, living things produce wastes that they must excrete, or eliminate, along the way. So food-getting, digestion, cellular respiration, and excretion are other important life processes common to living things.

A living thing may be composed of only one cell, like an amoeba, or millions of cells, like an elephant! But both the single-celled amoeba and the multicellular elephant perform all of the same life processes. Of course, they don't perform them all in exactly the same way because their body structures are so different.

The organisms you will investigate in this module will vary in size, shape, and complexity—like the amoeba and the elephant. They all have something in common—the ability to perform life processes to stay alive and healthy and to produce more of their own species.

Now that you know what makes something living, it becomes obvious why some things are nonliving. Nonliving things cannot perform life processes on their own. ☐

This robot is able to perform some of the same tasks as humans. What makes this robot different from a human being?

What's in an Organism's Name?

Even if you didn't know much about biology, you probably could guess that lions and tigers are close relatives. You also could be pretty sure that bears are animals and that roses are plants. It's easy because these organisms are familiar to us and have such distinctive appearances.

What if you had to find out whether mice, elephants, and bats were related? To answer this question, you would turn to taxonomy.

Taxonomy is the science of classifying living things. Taxonomy is based on the principle that everything in our world is related in some way. It is a science that groups organisms according to their structures and functions.

Taxonomy was introduced in the 18th century by Carolus Linnaeus, a Swedish scientist. Linnaeus's interest in taxonomy started early. His father had a large garden, and he introduced his

These animals look very different, but they've got enough in common to be in the same biological class. Can you identify their common features?

son to the science of plants. Linnaeus enjoyed studying plants, but even as a boy, he recognized that little information was available about how to classify plants. He saw a need for a universal classification system that would allow all scientists to communicate with one another about living things in a meaningful way.

While still in college, Linnaeus began to develop a method of classifying living things. In 1735, he published his first book on the subject, *Systema Naturae.* Over the years, he expanded the science of taxonomy, developing many of the methods still used today.

Carolus Linnaeus

A Seven-Layer System

Linnaeus developed rules for classifying plants and animals according to their structures. His work resulted in a seven-layer system: kingdom, phylum, class, order, family, genus, and species.

You can think of the system as an upside-down triangle. The top layer of the triangle is the kingdom category. Each kingdom contains the greatest number and diversity of organisms of the entire system. Because this layer is the largest, the organisms in it have fewer features in common than do organisms in the six other layers. For example, creatures as different as jellyfish and lions are both part of the Animal Kingdom. As you move down the triangle, fewer organisms are included in each category, but the organisms within each category have more features in common.

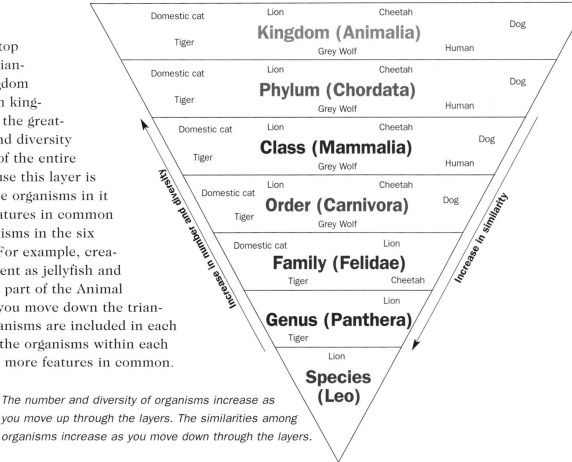

The number and diversity of organisms increase as you move up through the layers. The similarities among organisms increase as you move down through the layers.

Look at Table 1.1. You will see that all of the organisms listed across the top of the table are in the same kingdom, phylum, and class. With the exception of humans, they are also in the same order. The dog and grey wolf are in a different family than the four cats. And, of the four cats, only the tiger and the lion are in the same genus. The lion has the species name *leo*, which makes it unique from all the other animals in the chart.

Using Linnaeus's system, ants and spiders are part of the animal kingdom. They are also both members of the phylum Arthropoda (arthrop-OH-dah) because they have jointed legs. But each is in a different class. Ants are in the class of animals with three-part bodies and six legs. This class is called Insecta. Spiders are in the class of eight-legged organisms with two-part bodies. This class is known as Arachnida (ah-RAK-nî-dah).

Adding New Kingdoms

Linnaeus grouped all organisms into two main kingdoms—Plants and Animals. Until the second half of the 20th century, most biologists used his system. Then they added a third kingdom, the Protists, because microorganisms did not all clearly fit into the Animal or Plant kingdoms. As scientists discovered more and more information about organisms, they added two more kingdoms—Fungi and Monerans.

One Organism, Two Names

Linnaeus also developed a system for naming organisms, under which a two-part scientific name is assigned to every organism. An organism is named on the basis of its genus and species. The species name is usually an adjective, and the genus name is usually a noun. The first letter of the genus name is always capitalized. When the scientific name is typed, it is always in italics. When written by hand, it is underlined.

Some organisms are named after one of their prominent features. The scientific name for the red maple, for example, is *Acer rubrum*. *Acer* means "maple," and *rubrum* means "red." Some are named after the location in

Table 1.1 The Seven-Layer System

	Domestic cat	Lion	Cheetah	Tiger	Dog	Grey Wolf	Human
Kingdom	Animalia	Animalia	Animalia	Animalia	Animalia	Animalia	Animalia
Phylum	Chordata	Chordata	Chordata	Chordata	Chordata	Chordata	Chordata
Class	Mammalia	Mammalia	Mammalia	Mammalia	Mammalia	Mammalia	Mammalia
Order	Carnivora	Carnivora	Carnivora	Carnivora	Carnivora	Carnivora	Primates
Family	Felidae	Felidae	Felidae	Felidae	Canidae	Canidae	Hominidae
Genus	*Felis*	*Panthera*	*Acinonyx*	*Panthera*	*Canis*	*Canis*	*Homo*
Species	*silvestris*	*leo*	*jubatus*	*tigris*	*familiaris*	*lupus*	*sapiens*

which they are found. A species of fly discovered in Humbug Creek, California, was named *Oligodranes humbug.* Others are named after the scientist who discovered them.

There are other sources of names, too. There is a spider, *Draculoides bramstokeri,* named after the novel, *Dracula,* by Bram Stoker. Perhaps the grandfather of all names belongs to an aphid, a tiny insect. Its scientific name is *Myzocallis kahawaluokalani.* This Hawaiian name supposedly means, "You fish on your side of the lagoon and I'll fish on the other, and no one will fish in the middle."

Linnaeus's groundbreaking work of the 18th century remains the basis of the system we use today. Taxonomy now helps scientists to classify more than 10 million species of organisms on Earth and new kinds are discovered every year. Taxonomy is likely to continue to evolve as scientists debate the most appropriate classification system and the need to change that system to reflect new information and discovery. ☐

Their three-part body and six legs put ants in phylum Arthropoda and class Insecta. The two large sections at each end are the head and abdomen. The smaller segments in between comprise a third part, the thorax.

The two-part body and eight legs identify this spider as belonging to phylum Arthropoda, class Arachnida.

The WOWBug: Getting a Closer Look

A compound light microscope estimated to be 40–50 years old

COURTESY OF HENRY MILNE/© NSRC

INTRODUCTION

Many of the organisms pictured on the organism photo cards in Lesson 1 cannot be seen very well, or at all, with the naked eye. Those photos were made with the aid of magnification. To view the organisms yourself, you would use a microscope. In this lesson, you will learn how to prepare a dry-mount slide and how to use a compound light microscope to observe organisms. You will also learn how to prepare scientific drawings according to a specific set of guidelines, which you will use throughout the module. You will learn these skills while observing and learning about an interesting organism called the "WOWBug," a tiny wasp that is harmless to humans.

OBJECTIVES FOR THIS LESSON

Learn the parts of a microscope, and practice manipulating them to obtain the best image of slide-mounted specimens.

Measure the diameter of the field of view under different magnifications of the compound microscope.

Learn how to handle, manipulate, and recapture WOWBugs.

Prepare dry-mount slides of live WOWBugs.

Observe WOWBug grooming behavior.

Draw, label, and measure a WOWBug, following specific guidelines for scientific drawings.

Update your organism photo card for WOWBugs.

THROUGH THE COMPOUND EYE

For thousands of years, human beings have used tools. For a biologist, one of the most important tools is the microscope. Since its invention in the early 1600s, the microscope has been transformed into a relatively inexpensive, yet efficient, way for scientists such as yourself to view a world invisible to the naked eye.

You probably will use a compound light microscope during this module. In this type of microscope, light is provided either by a mirror or a small, built-in lightbulb. The word "compound" refers to the two lenses—one in the eyepiece and one in an objective—that together magnify the image. You can calculate the total magnification by multiplying the magnification of the lens of the eyepiece by that of the lens in the objective.

The drawing on page 14 shows the parts of a compound microscope and explains the function of each part.

As you use your microscope during this module, you will gain a working knowledge of its parts and their functions and become much more proficient at using this important tool of science.

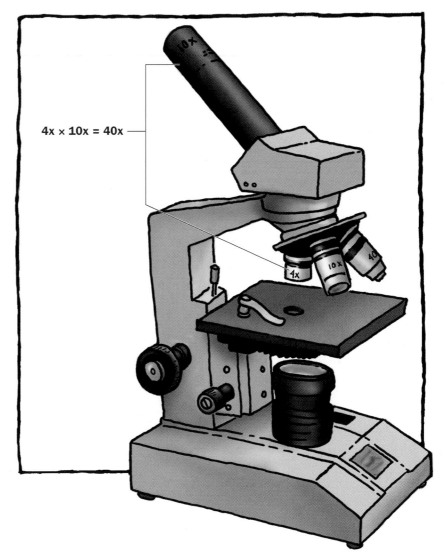

4x × 10x = 40x

Since the eyepiece is 10x and the objective is 4x, the total magnification of these two lenses used together is 40x.

(continued)

(continued from pg. 13)

The compound light microscope

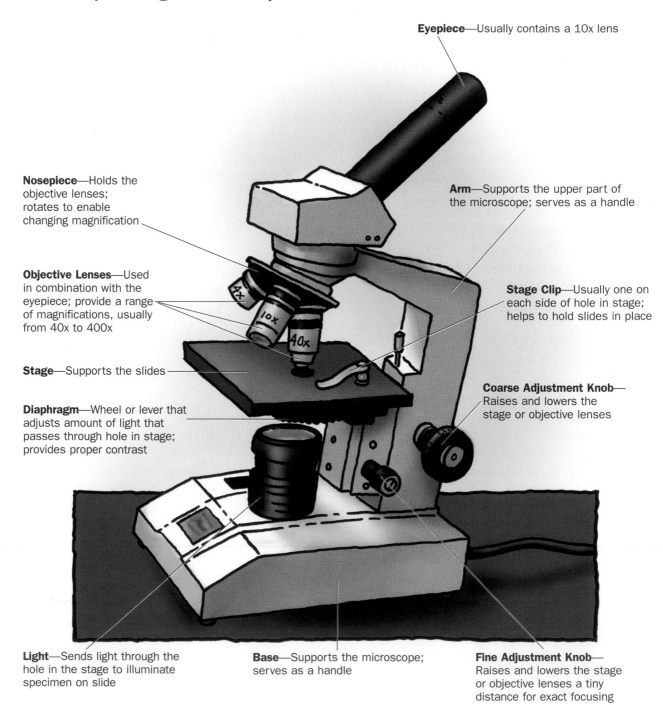

Eyepiece—Usually contains a 10x lens

Nosepiece—Holds the objective lenses; rotates to enable changing magnification

Arm—Supports the upper part of the microscope; serves as a handle

Objective Lenses—Used in combination with the eyepiece; provide a range of magnifications, usually from 40x to 400x

Stage Clip—Usually one on each side of hole in stage; helps to hold slides in place

Stage—Supports the slides

Coarse Adjustment Knob—Raises and lowers the stage or objective lenses

Diaphragm—Wheel or lever that adjusts amount of light that passes through hole in stage; provides proper contrast

Light—Sends light through the hole in the stage to illuminate specimen on slide

Base—Supports the microscope; serves as a handle

Fine Adjustment Knob—Raises and lowers the stage or objective lenses a tiny distance for exact focusing

Getting Started

1. Working in groups, observe your hand lens. Notice the shape of each lens. They are called "convex lenses" because they bulge in the middle and taper toward the edge. Stand at your desk and hold a hand lens about 1 centimeter (cm) above a line of text in your Student Guide.

2. In your science notebook, make a quick sketch of the hand lens, showing the appearance of the text through each of its lenses. Record your estimates of the magnifications directly on the corresponding lenses in your sketch. For example, if you estimated that one of the lenses magnified the text to two times its normal size, you would write 2× on that part of your sketch.

3. Center the smaller lens on top of the word "of" in this sentence. Close one eye, but continue to stare at the word "of." Slowly raise the lens from the page toward your open eye. Answer the following question in your science notebook:

   A. How does the image of the word "of" change as you raise the lens?

4. Repeat Step 3, but stop raising the lens when the word "of" appears upside down and backward, while still remaining in focus. Pick up the second hand lens. Center its larger lens directly over the small lens of the first hand lens, which should still be focused on the word "of." Look through the large lens while you raise it slowly. Keep your head up. If you put your eye down to the lens you will not

MATERIALS FOR LESSON 2

For you

- 1 copy of Student Sheet 2.3A: Guidelines for Scientific Drawings
- 1 copy of Student Sheet 2.3B: Drawing Your WOWBug

For your group

- 2 compound light microscopes
- 2 depression slides
- 2 plastic slides
- 4 hand lenses
- 5 WOWBugs
- 2 pipe cleaners
- 1 sheet of notebook paper
- 2 pieces of transparent tape
- 2 transparent rulers
- 2 metric rulers, 30 cm (12 in.)
- 1 plastic cup with lid, 4 oz
- 1 plastic cup of flour
- 4 No. 2 pencils
- 2 toothpicks
- 1 box of colored pencils
- 1 set of organism photo cards

see the intended effect. Answer the following question in your science notebook:

B. What happens to the image of the word "of" in the larger lens as you raise it away from the smaller lens?

5. With a partner, take a close look at your microscope. Refer to the reading selection "Through the Compound Eye," which you read for homework, to identify the microscope's main parts and to find out how to calculate the magnifications you would get using its different lenses. Discuss with your group how two lenses work together in a microscope to produce an image.

Inquiry 2.1
Corralling Your WOWBugs

PROCEDURE

1. Place a piece of notebook paper in front of your group. Your teacher will put about five female WOWBugs on the paper.

2. Have one member of the group very gently corral the WOWBugs into the center of the paper using the tip of the pipe cleaner, as seen in Figure 2.1. A gentle nudge of the pipe cleaner will stimulate the WOWBugs to change direction. After about 30 seconds, quickly pass the pipe cleaner to another group member. Have this member continue to corral the WOWBugs into the center of the paper. Continue until all group members have had a turn.

3. While the last group member is practicing handling the WOWBugs, have another group member carefully invert the plastic cup over each WOWBug, one at a time, until they have all crawled up on its inside surface. Save for Inquiry 2.2.

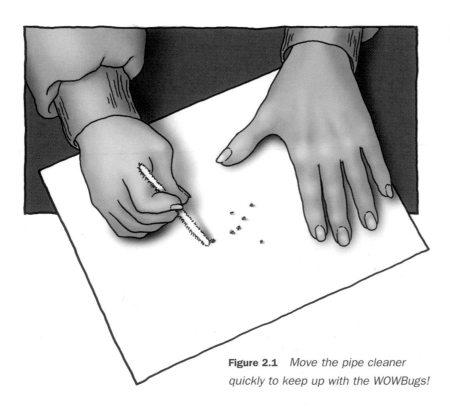

Figure 2.1 *Move the pipe cleaner quickly to keep up with the WOWBugs!*

Inquiry 2.2
Preparing a Dry-Mount Slide To View WOWBug Grooming Behavior

PROCEDURE

1. Working with a partner, take the following steps to prepare a dry-mount slide of a WOWBug:

A. Place a depression slide on the notebook paper. Keep handy a flat, plastic slide and two 2-cm pieces of transparent tape.

B. Dip a toothpick into the container of flour supplied by your teacher. Then tap a few specks of the flour into the well of the depression slide. Stir the flour with the tip of the toothpick to scatter it around the depression. Use just enough flour dust so that the WOWBug becomes slightly "dirty." Too much flour could harm the WOWBug.

C. Use the pipe cleaner to remove one WOWBug from the cup and transfer it into the slide's depression. Quickly place the flat, plastic slide on top of it, trapping the WOWBug in the depression.

D. Use the two pieces of transparent tape to fasten the ends of the slides together to prevent the WOWBug from escaping. Your slide should look like the one in Figure 2.2.

2. Take the following steps to view the dry-mount slide:

A. Place the dry-mount slide on the microscope stage and focus on the WOWBug under the lowest magnification. If the WOWBug is moving around, practice keeping it in the field of view by moving the slide slowly and smoothly with your fingers while you observe it through the eyepiece. If you are lucky, you may get to see the WOWBug standing still to clean the flour from its legs or antennae. Note

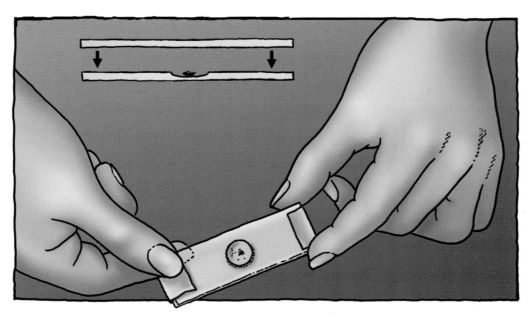

Figure 2.2 *Fasten the tape securely or the WOWBug might escape!*

whether it cleans away the specks of flour in any particular order or manner.

B. Repeat Procedure Step 2A with each of the other objective lenses until you have viewed the WOWBug under all magnifications.

C. Have your partner repeat Procedure steps 2A and 2B.

3. Save the slide for Inquiry 2.3.

Inquiry 2.3
Preparing Scientific Drawings of the WOWBug

PROCEDURE

1. Listen while your teacher reviews the information on Student Sheet 2.3A: Guidelines for Scientific Drawings.

2. Have one student in your pair place your WOWBug dry-mount slide on the microscope stage.

3. Draw the WOWBug in the top circle on Student Sheet 2.3B, following the guidelines on Student Sheet 2.3A. Include as much detail as you can. Take turns with your partner at the microscope. The WOWBug should stand relatively still while cleaning itself, so you can pay close attention to details like the number of parts in the antennae or legs. Use the highest magnification through which you can see the entire WOWBug in greatest detail. This should be the one in which the WOWBug nearly fills the field of view. Since the WOWBug is three dimensional, you may find that you have to adjust the fine focus at times to see the various structures more clearly.

4. Normally, as you view the WOWBug through the microscope, it will be right side up so that you would be looking at its back, which scientists call its dorsum. If the WOWBug is walking upside down on the top cover, you will see its underside, which is called its venter. If this happens, flip the slide over on the stage and observe it from the other side. Title your drawing, "WOWBug—Dorsal View."

5. If the WOWBug is too active and repeatedly crawls out of the field of view, try viewing the slide prepared by the other pair in your group. If you still can't see the WOWBug, ask your teacher for assistance.

6. Label at least five structures. Refer to the illustration of the WOWBug in the reading selection "Intriguing Insects" for names of its structures.

7. To complete your drawing, it is necessary to give the viewer or reader some idea of the size of the WOWBug. After following the steps below, you will better understand the relative sizes of different kinds of organisms when given a drawing of them.

A. Remove the slide from the microscope stage, and switch the magnification to the lowest power.

B. Center the transparent ruler on the stage and count the number of millimeter (mm) lines you can see across the widest part of the field of view. Record this number on Student Sheet 2.3B on the line next to this label: Diameter of Field of View (mm) at Low Magnification.

C. Switch the magnification to medium power, and repeat your measurement.

Record this number next to the label: Diameter of the Field of View (mm) at Medium Magnification.

D. Switch the magnification to the highest power, and repeat this process once more. Record this number on your student sheet next to this label: Diameter of the Field of View (mm) at High Magnification (400×, 430×, or whichever is greatest on your microscope.)

E. Remove the ruler. Switch the magnification to the lowest power, put the slide back on the stage, and focus on the WOWBug. Based on the number of ruler lines you counted under the lowest magnification, estimate the length of the

WOWBug in mm. Record this number on your student sheet next to this label: Estimated WOWBug Body Length (mm) at Low Magnification.

F. Now place the ruler underneath the slide until the tip of one end of the WOWBug is right in the center of one of the mm marks, as shown in Figure 2.3.

G. Measure the actual body length of the WOWBug in mm, and record that length on your student sheet next to the label: Actual WOWBug Body Length (mm) at Low Magnification. Also record the length on Student Sheet 2.3B, just to the right of the drawing's title. Check the actual measurement against your estimate.

Figure 2.3 *You can only measure the length of the WOWBug accurately when it is positioned correctly against a mm mark of the ruler.*

8. When you and your partner have completed your drawings, review the 10 guidelines on Student Sheet 2.3A. When you are satisfied that you have correctly followed these guidelines, trade drawings with your partner. Notice that the numbers 1–10 are listed below the Title line of your drawing. These represent the drawing guidelines. Circle, in pencil, the number of each guideline that your partner did not follow. Then, assign each other's drawing a score of 1 to 10, based on the number of guidelines that were followed correctly. When you are both finished, return each other's drawings. Revise your drawing and give it back to your partner to review again. Erase the circle around each number of a guideline that was revised correctly. Continue until you both earn 10 points. This process is called peer evaluation. It is an important part of scientific inquiry.

9. Focus the microscope on one structure of the WOWBug (an antenna, a wing, or a leg, for example) using the highest magnification possible. Draw that structure in the second circle on Student Sheet 2.3B. Give it an appropriate title, and label anything on this structure that you found in the illustration of a WOWBug in the reading selection "Intriguing Insects," which you read for homework. Peer-evaluate this drawing before turning it in, if you wish.

10. Update your organism photo card for the WOWBug.

REFLECTING ON WHAT YOU'VE DONE
On the basis of what you have learned in this lesson, answer the following questions on Student Sheet 2.3B. Be prepared to discuss your answers with the class.

A. Explain two ways in which the compound light microscope is an improvement over the microscope developed by Antony van Leeuwenhoek.

B. List three ways in which lenses are used as tools of science, in addition to their use in compound microscopes.

C. How did the diameter of the field of view change when you changed the microscope's objective lenses?

D. What characteristics of the WOWBug did you observe that suggest it is an insect?

E. In what ways did your WOWBug remove the flour dust from its body? List two reasons why you think grooming would be important to a WOWBug. (Hint: Why is grooming important for you?)

F. According to the reading selection "Intriguing Insects," how are parasitic wasps, such as WOWBugs, important to humans?

Intriguing Insects

When you think about insects, which come to mind first? Butterflies? Ants? Bees? In fact, beetles are the most common insect. If you lined up every kind of plant and animal in a row, every fourth organism would likely be a beetle. And beetles are only one kind of insect!

There are hundreds of types of insects on Earth, ranging from the common to the exotic. You're probably quite familiar with wasps, flies, mosquitoes, moths, crickets, fireflies, and dragonflies. Have you ever heard of a cicada known as the "buffalo head" because its head resembles a buffalo's, complete with a set of horns? Or the whirligig beetle, which uses its two sets of eyes in a clever way when it goes swimming? One set looks above the water's surface, while the other checks out the action below. And don't forget the fruit fly, *Drosophila.* The scientific study of the brief life cycle of this tiny fly laid the groundwork for modern genetics.

What do all of these insects have in common? They all have three distinct body parts—a head, a thorax, and an abdomen. They also have six legs, four wings, and an outer covering called an "exoskeleton."

When you think about it, insects are just about everywhere. They live in our houses, in our gardens, on our pets, and sometimes even on us. You find them in lakes, ponds, and streams. They survive on the coldest mountains and in the hottest deserts.

These are just a few of the thousands of varieties of beetles found all over the world.

CHIP CLARK, NATIONAL MUSEUM OF NATURAL HISTORY, SMITHSONIAN INSTITUTION

Good Guys and Bad Guys

Some people don't like insects at all. However, each kind of insect has a role to play in the world, and each affects our lives in a different way.

Some insects seem to cause more than their share of trouble. According to Dr. Robert Matthews, a professor at the University of Georgia, insects have caused an enormous amount of human suffering. Some mosquitoes transmit diseases, like malaria and yellow fever, which are major threats to human health in much of the world. Flying grasshoppers called migratory locusts destroy entire fields of crops.

We consider other insects to be good guys. Honeybees pollinate the flowers of many of our favorite food crops. Anyone who has enjoyed a biscuit with honey also appreciates their efforts.

Less familiar insects, such as parasitic wasps, lay their eggs in or on other insects. A parasite is an organism that obtains its nutrients from another organism, generally damaging the other organism in the process.

A World Without Wasps

Parasites may sound destructive, but they also play an important role. For example, a world without parasitic wasps would be a very different place. These insects help lower Earth's pest population. In fact, scientists have calculated that a single pair of houseflies, if left alone, could potentially produce enough descendants in a year to cover the surface of the earth several centimeters deep. Fortunately, this doesn't happen, thanks to natural enemies such as parasitic wasps, which kill large numbers of flies every year. ☐

Few crops can stand up to a swarm of insects such as this.

As you can see, grasshoppers can do considerable damage to a field of corn.

Dr. Matthews and the WOWBug

Dr. Matthews, second from left, sharing a butterfly collection with members of the WOWBugs team.

These WOWBugs are only 1.5 millimeters long, but they play a very large role in helping to control bee and fly populations. Female (left); male (right). Note the male's unusual antennae.

Dr. Robert Matthews is an entomologist, a scientist who studies insects. He has studied insects for many years and in many parts of the world.

One of Dr. Matthews's favorite insects is a small parasitic wasp called *Melittobia digitata.* That's quite a mouthful, which is why Dr. Matthews nicknamed it the "WOWBug." He and his students have learned much about the strange habits of this intriguing insect. Through their efforts, the WOWBug has become one of the newest organisms studied in the science classroom.

What's so special about WOWBugs? And how did they make their way into the classroom? It was an unlikely beginning. Dr. Matthews did not find the bugs—they found him! While he was a graduate student, Dr. Matthews decided to examine the nests of some little wild bees he found outdoors. He took the nests inside and put them on a shelf in his laboratory. Later, he got the nests down to study them. To his surprise, he found not little bees, but WOWBugs! Unnoticed, they had sneaked into the nests, fed, and multiplied. They had destroyed nearly all of his bees, and Dr. Matthews was pretty angry.

Many years later, while thinking about new ways to teach biology, Dr. Matthews remembered the WOWBug. He realized that the same WOWBug behaviors

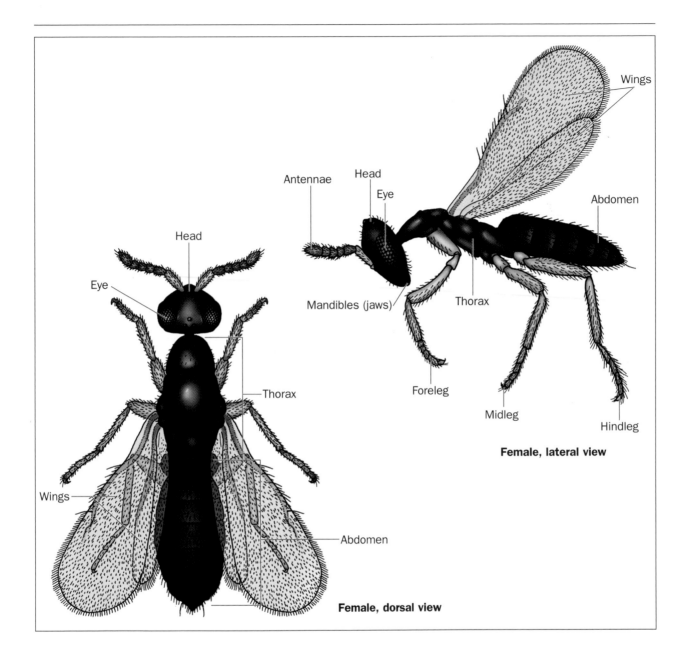

Female, dorsal view

Female, lateral view

that nearly ruined his early research would make these little parasites wonderful in the science classroom. WOWBugs breed easily in large numbers, they have a very short life cycle, and they don't take up much space. Best of all, they can't hurt humans with their stingers.

As he worked with WOWBugs, Dr. Matthews continued to learn new and fascinating things about their biology and behavior. He wanted to share what he was learning. With the help of other scientists and teachers, Dr. Matthews developed a set of teaching activities to help students learn science concepts and skills by working with WOWBugs.

Scientists on the WOWBugs team at the University of Georgia continue to make new discoveries every day. They write a newsletter, give workshops for teachers, and develop new lab investigations. If you'd like to learn about the latest developments on WOWBugs, visit the STC/MS™ Web site (http://www.stcms.si.edu) to find a link to the WOWBugs Web site. ☐

MICROSCOPE PIONEERS

You can't study organisms thoroughly without a good microscope. This tool, which today's scientists take for granted, has played a major role in helping scientists understand more about living things.

Robert Hooke and Antony van Leeuwenhoek (Lay-ven-HOKE) were important pioneers in the development of this important scientific instrument. Hooke was born in England in 1635. A member of the Royal Society of England, he was one of the most famous scientists of his time. Leeuwenhoek was born in the Dutch town of Delft in 1632.

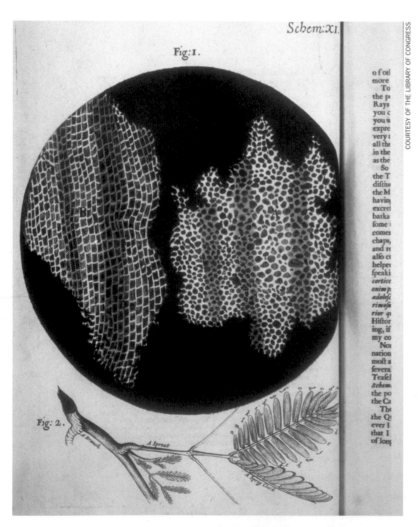

Cork cells as seen by Robert Hooke

Hooke: Discovering the Mysteries of Cork

Today, Robert Hooke is remembered more as a mathematician than as a biologist. But like all scientists of his day, he had broad interests. He made many contributions to biology. In his book, *Micrographia,* Hooke described and illustrated the discoveries he had made using a compound microscope that he'd built. Hooke used the microscope to observe familiar objects such as insects, sponges, and feathers. When he put a thin slice of cork under the lens of his microscope, Hooke made a very important discovery. He saw the cell walls in the cork tissue. Hooke had discovered plant cells.

Even though his discoveries were amazing in his day, Hooke's microscope was quite crude. It didn't look that different from today's microscopes, but it had poorly ground lenses, which caused Hooke's view of the objects to be blurred or distorted. What's more, early microscopes could not magnify objects more than 20 or 30 times their actual size. By contrast, most microscopes found in middle schools today can magnify objects up to 430 times.

Leeuwenhoek Perfects the Lens

Leeuwenhoek's major contribution to the development of the microscope was to make lenses that were much more finely ground than those used by Hooke and others. He never went to college, and he earned a living by selling fabric in a small shop. For him, making microscopes was a hobby that became a lifelong obsession.

Leeuwenhoek learned to grind lenses by observing the craftsmen who made eyeglasses in Delft. Leeuwenhoek's lenses, often no more than 0.3 centimeters across, were so even and perfect they provided clear images that were free of distortion. They could magnify objects to between 50 and 300 times their actual size. He mounted the tiny lenses in frames of gold and silver that he also crafted himself.

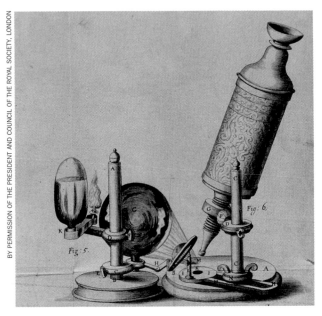

Hooke's microscope was called a "compound micro-scope" because it had two lenses.

Leeuwenhoek's microscope

Unlike Hooke's compound microscope, Leeuwenhoek's device had only one lens. It was mounted in a tiny hole in a brass plate. Leeuwenhoek placed the object he wanted to examine on a sharp point in front of the lens. He adjusted the position with the screws. The entire device was less than 10 centimeters long.

For a scientist, good tools are just the start. Scientists also need the ability to observe carefully and to record their findings accurately. They need patience. Leeuwenhoek had all these qualities; in addition, he was very curious. He wrote about everything he saw, from algae on pond water to mineral crystals and fossils. He discovered microscopic organisms in rainwater. He discovered blood cells and was the first to see living sperm in an insect. He is credited with publishing the first drawing of bacteria.

Leeuwenhoek stuck just about everything under his lens—including plaque from his own teeth! What did he see? Something that wouldn't surprise your dentist at all. "I saw . . . many very little living animalcules," he wrote. "Very prettily a-moving. The biggest . . . had a very strong and swift motion . . . and shot through the water. The second . . . spun around like a top."

Hooke passed away in 1703, and Leeuwenhoek died in 1723, at the age of 91. Both had become world famous. Leeuwenhoek was so famous that Peter the Great, czar of Russia, once came to Delft to visit him at his home.

The science of microscopy has made great progress since the time of Hooke and Leeuwenhoek. To get an idea of how much progress, take a look at the image of a mite. It was taken through a scanning electron microscope that has a magnification range of from 15 to 200,000 times! ☐

This mite, which measures 150–200 microns in length ($\frac{1}{1000}$ mm), is magnified 850 times its actual size.

Investigating *Lumbriculus*

If these students looked carefully through the mud in the shallow areas of this pond, they might be surprised at the number of blackworms they would find.

DWIGHT R. KUHN

INTRODUCTION

In this lesson, you will work with an organism called *Lumbriculus variegatus,* also known as the California blackworm. You will observe the structure of a blackworm with a hand lens and decide which familiar organism it most resembles. You will also try to identify its anterior (head) and posterior (tail) ends. You'll observe this creature more closely through the microscope and prepare a scientific drawing using the skills and techniques you learned in Lesson 2. You will observe blood pulsating through its blood vessels and measure its average pulse rate. Then you will be given a small fragment of a blackworm to observe and measure. You will place the fragment in a small plastic tube and observe it over 3 weeks for signs of change. Finally, you will update your group's organism photo card for the blackworm.

OBJECTIVES FOR THIS LESSON

Observe, sketch, and measure a blackworm, and compare its structure to that of a related organism.

Measure and record the average pulse rate of a blackworm.

Make observations of a blackworm fragment each week for 3 weeks to look for signs of change.

Update your organism photo card for blackworms.

Getting Started

1. You will begin this lesson by working with your partner to make some brief observations of a blackworm. You will then work with your group and class to answer several questions.

2. Work with your partner to prepare either a petri dish lid or base to hold your blackworm. One pair of students will work with the top of a petri dish; the other pair will use the base. Each pair will use one piece of filter paper.

A. If your pair is using the petri dish lid, place the filter paper into the lid, but do not trim the paper.

B. If your pair is using the petri dish base, place it upside down on the filter paper. Trace a circle on the filter paper. Quickly cut out the circle and trim it so that it fits comfortably inside the dish. Place the circle in the dish.

3. Take your petri dish and filter paper to the blackworm culture container your teacher has prepared. Follow your teacher's directions to obtain a blackworm. Do not mix in water or chemicals from any other sources or you risk killing the blackworms.

MATERIALS FOR LESSON 3

For you

1 copy of Student Sheet 3.1: Template for Blackworm Drawing

1 copy of Student Sheet 3.2: Average Pulse Rate of a Blackworm

1 copy of Student Sheet 3.3: Observations of Blackworm Fragments

For your group

1 set of organism photo cards

1 petri dish lid or base

2 metric rulers, 30 cm (12 in.)

2 stopwatches

2 blackworms

2 hand lenses

2 plastic pipettes

2 microcentrifuge tubes

1 pair of scissors

2 compound light microscopes

4 pieces of filter paper

2 plastic slides

1 black marker

4. Take turns with your partner, using your hand lens to briefly observe the blackworm.

5. Work with your group to answer the following questions in your science notebook. Take another look at the blackworm if necessary.

A. What familiar organism does the blackworm resemble?

B. In what way(s) does the blackworm resemble this organism?

C. In what way(s) is it different from this organism?

D. Explain how you can tell the anterior end from the posterior end of your blackworm.

6. Share your answers with the class.

Inquiry 3.1
Drawing and Measuring a Blackworm

PROCEDURE

1. If necessary, use your pipette to dampen the filter paper with a few drops of water from the culture container. Place the petri dish on the microscope stage and focus on the blackworm under a total magnification of 40× (see Figure 3.1).

2. Prepare a detailed drawing of your blackworm on Student Sheet 3.1: Template for Blackworm Drawing, as the student is doing in Figure 3.2. Follow the guidelines for scientific drawings that you learned in Lesson 2. Title your drawing, "*Lumbriculus*: The California Blackworm."

COURTESY OF HENRY MILNE/© NSRC

Figure 3.1 *The translucent quality of the blackworm's skin allows you to see the blood vessels and digestive tube quite clearly.*

COURTESY OF HENRY MILNE/© NSRC

Figure 3.2 *Refer to the directions for scientific drawings when you draw and label your blackworm.*

3. Label at least three structures of the blackworm on your drawing. Use the reading selection "More Than Just Bait" at the end of this lesson as a reference.

4. Follow these instructions to measure your blackworm:

A. Take out a piece of unused notebook paper and lay it on your desk.

B. Fill about one-third of your pipette with spring water from the blackworm culture container. Take it back to your desk and squirt the water into the petri dish containing the blackworm.

C. Tilt the petri dish to move the water around until the blackworm is soaked. Use your pipette to suck up the blackworm with a small amount of water.

D. Slowly and carefully squirt the water with the blackworm onto the notebook paper to form one large drop. Use the tip of the pipette to draw the water out in one direction. The blackworm will spread out to follow the trail of water, as shown in Figure 3.3.

E. Once the blackworm has spread out fully, measure it with the metric ruler. Be careful not to touch the blackworm or you may damage it. Record your measurement in the appropriate place on Student Sheet 3.1.

5. Use your pipette to suck up the blackworm from the notebook paper and squirt it back into the petri dish.

Figure 3.3 *Slowly draw out the drop of water using the tip of the plastic pipette.*

Inquiry 3.2
Determining the Pulse Rate of a Blackworm

PROCEDURE

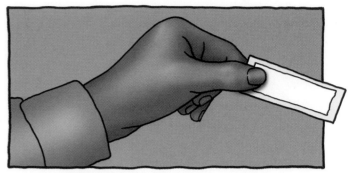

Figure 3.4 *Make sure the piece of filter paper is a little narrower than the slide.*

1. Use your scissors to cut a piece of filter paper into a rectangular shape that will fit on a microscope slide, as seen in Figure 3.4.

2. Use your pipette to obtain a few drops of water from the culture container. Place the filter paper on the slide, and use the water to dampen the paper. Using your pipette, transfer the blackworm from the petri dish to the slide. Place the slide on your microscope stage. Focus on a small section of the blackworm under the lowest power (40×). You should be able to see the blood moving through the vessels.

   Agree with your group on how to describe the movement of blood in your blackworm.

3. Pulse rate in blackworms can be defined as the number of pulsations of blood that pass by one location in 1 minute. Decide with your partner how you will measure the pulse rate of your blackworm.

   Think about the variables involved in this investigation. Discuss what you will keep constant each time you measure the pulse rate.

4. Set up a data table on Student Sheet 3.2: Average Pulse Rate of a Blackworm on which to record your data. Leave enough space for several trials. This will ensure more valid results.

5. Take turns with your partner counting the pulsations of blood and watching the clock or stopwatch. Record your information in your data table. After you have completed the counts, find the average pulse rate for your blackworm. If you have difficulty finding a pulse in your blackworm because it is moving around too much, ask your teacher to let you try a different blackworm that may be less active.

6. Follow your teacher's directions for returning your organism. Dispose of your filter paper, and return your petri dish and microscope slide to the plastic box.

COURTESY OF HENRY MILNE/© NSRC

Figure 3.5 *These students are working together to measure the pulse rate of their blackworm.*

Inquiry 3.3
Investigating Regeneration of Blackworms

PROCEDURE

1. Use a marker to label a small plastic tube with your group's name and class period. Use a plastic pipette to fill the plastic tube with water from the blackworm culture container. Snap the cap shut and set the tube aside.

2. Prepare a microscope slide and filter paper as you did in Procedure Steps 1 and 2 of Inquiry 3.2.

3. On Student Sheet 3.3: Observations of Blackworm Fragments, prepare a data table for recording your observations on four different dates over 3 weeks. Include space for recording the date, number of segments, and length in your blackworm fragment.

4. Take your slide to your teacher to obtain a blackworm fragment.

5. Use the lowest power and the dimmest light of your microscope to view your fragment, measure its length, and count the number of segments. Record your observations on the data table you prepared on Student Sheet 3.3. Be aware that too much heat or light or excessive shaking could kill your blackworm fragment. Turn off the light immediately after counting the segments.

6. When you have completed your measurements, use a pipette to transfer the fragment to the plastic tube. Snap the cover on the tube and give the tube to your teacher for storage.

7. Work with your group to update the blackworm organism photo card.

REFLECTING ON WHAT YOU'VE DONE
On the basis of what you have learned in this lesson, respond to the following on the student sheets indicated:

A. Use a Venn diagram to summarize the similarities and differences between a blackworm and the common earthworm. (Student Sheet 3.1)

B. You may have noticed that one or both ends of some of the blackworms are lighter in color than the rest of their bodies. What is the probable reason for this? (Student Sheet 3.1)

C. Why do blackworms make some of their unusual movements? (Student Sheet 3.1)

D. What did the class discover about the pulse rate of your blackworm when it was measured at different parts of its body? (Student Sheet 3.2)

E. If you measured your pulse at different places on your body, would you expect to observe the same pattern of results? Explain. (Student Sheet 3.2)

F. Lisa says that, in addition to being fairly active, blackworms are much larger than organisms usually studied through the microscope. Because of this, she believes blackworms have a more complex way of moving food and oxygen through their bodies. What evidence have you observed to support Lisa's statement? (Student Sheet 3.2)

G. What evidence did you observe that regeneration has occurred in your blackworm? (Student Sheet 3.3)

More Than Just Bait

What do you get when you cut a blackworm in half?

A. One dead worm
B. Two live worms
C. A bloody mess

Strangely, the answer is B. This amazing worm, whose scientific name is *Lumbriculus variegatus,* can be cut into several fragments—and it won't die or even bleed. Instead, it regenerates a new head or tail, or both, from the various pieces.

What's more amazing is that the blackworm is not a rare animal living in some faraway place. Usually no more than 10 centimeters long, this worm lives in the shallow edges of ponds, marshes, and lakes throughout North America and Europe.

Despite its short length, a mature blackworm has between 150 and 250 body segments. Even a fragment of blackworm only a few segments long can regenerate lost body parts—fast. In fact, fragmentation, followed by regeneration, is much more common than sexual reproduction in blackworms.

"The segments regenerate quickly," says Dr. Charles Drewes, a zoologist who has studied blackworms for many years. "For example, a new head or tail usually develops within 2 to 3 weeks. The new segments—usually eight for a head and between 20 and 100 for a tail—are smaller and paler than the original ones."

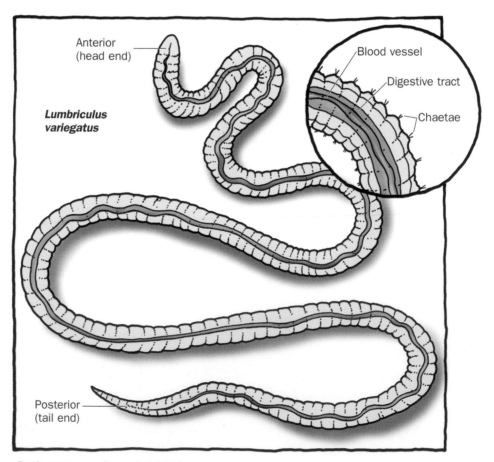

Basic anatomy of an adult blackworm

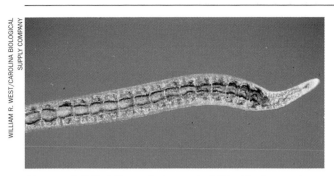

You can tell that the anterior end of this blackworm has undergone regeneration because of its pale color.

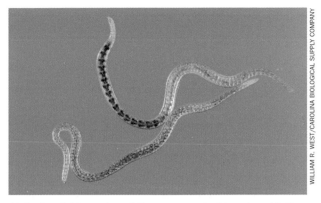

Note the lighter color of the regenerated head and tail ends of these blackworms.

A Worm With a Rapid Reflex

The blackworm "swims" by twisting its body through the water in a corkscrew fashion. If the water in which it lives is shallow enough, a blackworm will stretch its tail to the surface of the water. It then bends its tail at a right angle so that a few centimeters of its dorsal surface is lying just above the water's surface. Part of the tail now faces skyward and is exposed to air. Although this is a good position for gas exchange of oxygen and carbon dioxide, it exposes the blackworm's tail to its enemies.

To offset the problem of the tail's exposure, the worm uses a special rapid escape reflex. The tail end rapidly shortens in response to a threatening enemy. This reflex can be triggered by touch, a vibration, or even by the sudden appearance of a shadow. Nerve cells, called "photoreceptors," which are able to detect these shadows, are located in the blackworm's tail.

If you look closely, you can make out the tail of a blackworm bent to be parallel to the surface of this pond.

The bulge around the earthworm near its center is called the clitellum. It produces mucus that forms a cocoon for the worm's eggs.

It's All in the Family

If you haven't seen a blackworm in the wild, you've likely seen its relative, *Lumbricus terrestris,* the common earthworm. It, too, lives throughout North America and Europe—but in the soil. It can grow up to 25 centimeters long, and like the blackworm, it has the gift of regeneration.

A mature earthworm has about 150 segments. It also has a light-colored bulge on its body, called the clitellum. If an earthworm is cut in two, only the part with the clitellum can regenerate. The part without the clitellum will die.

The next time you see an earthworm, look for its clitellum. Look even more carefully and you'll also see tiny hairs on each segment of its body. These hairs, called setae (SEE-tee), help earthworms move by giving them many tiny grips on the soil. In blackworms, similar hairs are referred to as chaetae.

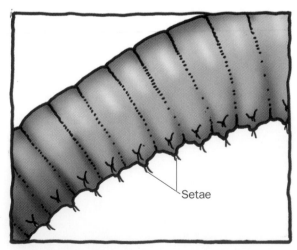

These tiny hairs help the earthworm cling to the soil as it moves.

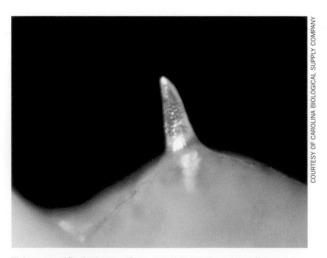

This magnified photo of an earthworm's seta allows you to see its actual structure.

Earth Movers

Earthworms have remarkable regeneration powers, and they are also terrific diggers. These mini-bulldozers actually plow and fertilize soil!

Here's how: First, they eat bits of soil, decaying leaves, and bacteria and other microorganisms. (Each bite enlarges their network of underground tunnels.) With digestive systems the length of their bodies, they next grind and mix their food. Then they expel their waste, called castings, which is actually first-rate, nutrient-rich soil. Throughout this process, these tiny farmers till the earth by bringing subsoil to the surface. That's not all! Their tunnels give air and water easy access to the roots of plants, helping them to grow.

Both blackworms and earthworms are amazing animals that deserve our respect. So while we may have to look down to find them, we should never look down on them. ☐

Are blackworms and earthworms the only two organisms that can undergo regeneration? Hardly! Another amazing regeneration story belongs to the starfish. A starfish can grow a new arm, or ray, if it loses one. A few starfish species can even regenerate an entire body from a single ray. In some cases, several starfish can result from one starfish that gets cut into pieces.

The shape of this starfish will become more typical as its parts regenerate fully.

DWIGHT R. KUHN

Creating Your Own Pond

Ponds are often the inspiration for great works of art, such as this painting by Claude Monet entitled The Japanese Footbridge.

© 2000 NATIONAL GALLERY OF ART, WASHINGTON, D.C.

INTRODUCTION

An ecosystem is a community that includes living things and their environment, functioning together as a unit. There are many kinds of ecosystems. In this lesson, you will create your own pond ecosystem and begin observing the living and nonliving things found there. You will complete your observations in Lesson 12.

OBJECTIVES FOR THIS LESSON

Construct a pond and observe, sketch, and label its layers.

Observe and document the living things in the pond, directly, and with magnification.

Explain the types of changes that may occur in your pond over a 3-week period.

Getting Started

1. Work with your group to develop a list of at least six organisms you might expect to find in and around a pond. Write this list in your science notebook.

2. Share your list with the class.

MATERIALS FOR LESSON 4

For your group

4 copies of Student Sheet 4.2: Sketches of Pond—Macro and Micro

1 clear plastic cup with lid

2 compound light microscopes

2 depression slides

2 coverslips

2 hand lenses

1 plastic pipette

2 pairs of scissors

1 small cotton ball

1 metric ruler, 30 cm (12 in.)

1 250-mL graduated cylinder

2 decaying leaves

2 pieces of hay

5 *Lemna* plants

5 grains of rice

1 black marker

1 box of colored pencils

Gravel

Soil

Spring water

Inquiry 4.1
Constructing Your Pond

PROCEDURE

1. Use the scoop to measure 50 cubic centimeters (cm³) of gravel into a graduated cylinder. (One cm³ is equivalent in volume to 1 milliliter [mL].) Pour the gravel into the plastic cup to form a layer on the bottom, as shown in Figure 4.1. Then, use the metric ruler and your marker to put a mark about 1.5 cm from the bottom of the cup.

2. Place soil on the gravel until it reaches that mark.

3. Use your scissors to cut the two leaves into smaller pieces and lay them flat on the surface of the soil and gravel.

4. Cut the hay into pieces about 5 cm long and place them on the leaves, as shown in Figure 4.2.

5. Gently pour into the cup approximately 350 mL of the water provided by your teacher.

6. Use the tip of your pipette to transfer five *Lemna* plants from the culture container to your pond. Using your hand lens, count the number of leaves, called "fronds," on the five plants. Record the number of fronds in your science notebook. You will need the number for Lesson 12.

Figure 4.1 *The gravel, as well as the cup bottom, provides a base for your pond.*

7. Your final product should look like the cup in Figure 4.2. Do not move the pond for several minutes. This will allow the soil to begin settling to the bottom.

8. Proceed to Inquiry 4.2 immediately after creating your pond.

Lemna

Water

Hay

Leaves

Soil

Gravel

Figure 4.2 *Lay the hay on top of the leaves. Then add water.*

Inquiry 4.2
Observing Your Pond

PROCEDURE

1. Observe your pond at eye level. In the box provided on Student Sheet 4.2: Sketches of Pond—Macro and Micro, sketch exactly what you see. Be very detailed about your observations. Label the layers you observe in the cup using the directions for scientific drawings that you were given in Lesson 2. Color your drawing as accurately as you can.

2. Prepare and view a slide of water from your pond in the following manner:

A. Add several strands of cotton to the depression in your slide. This helps slow the movement of any microorganisms that are present.

B. Use a plastic pipette to obtain water from the bottom of your pond, just above the soil and gravel. Add one drop of pond water to the depression on the slide.

C. Place a coverslip over the drop of water by placing one edge of the coverslip onto the slide and lowering the other edge slowly to avoid trapping air bubbles beneath, as illustrated in Figure 4.3. This type of slide is called a wet mount.

D. Set the magnification to 100×; then move the slide around while you look for microorganisms through the eyepiece of your microscope. Sketch in the circles on your student sheet any microorganisms that you may see.

3. Repeat Procedure Step 2 with a water sample from the top level of your pond. You will make further observations when you revisit your pond in a later lesson, so be as thorough as you can for comparison purposes.

4. Use the marker to write your group members' names near the top of your cup. Add five grains of rice to your pond; then place the lid loosely on top. This will slow down the evaporation of water as well as expose the water to oxygen.

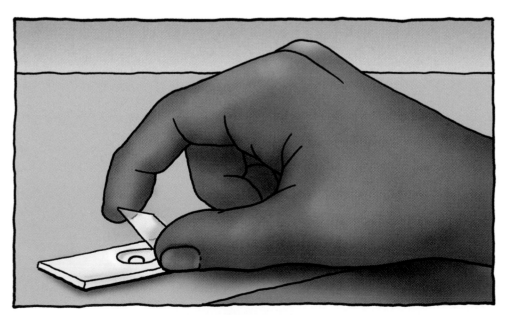

Figure 4.3 *Place one edge of the coverslip down first.*

5. Follow your teacher's directions for storing the pond and cleaning up.

REFLECTING ON WHAT YOU'VE DONE

1. Look back at the list you generated in your science notebook during "Getting Started." On the basis of what you have observed, revise your list.

2. Following your list of pond organisms in your science notebook, predict the ways in which you think your pond will change over the next 3 weeks.

EXCUSE ME,
But Your Habitat Is in My Ecosystem!

There are countless ecosystems in the world. An ecosystem can be as small as a puddle or as large as an ocean. An ecosystem can simply be a stretch of grassland or a rotten tree trunk. You'll find an ecosystem wherever groups of living and nonliving things interact.

In the ocean, which is a saltwater environment, bottle-nosed dolphins interact with squid—by eating them. Sea lions eat squid, too, so they compete with the dolphins. Since they all interact, bottle-nosed dolphins, squid, and sea lions all share the same ecosystem.

Rainbow trout, which live in cool, freshwater streams, share their ecosystem with plants and other organisms, including those they prey on, such as snails and dragonflies. Both the freshwater stream and the saltwater ocean are known as aquatic—or water-based—ecosystems.

Inside a Typical Ecosystem—A Pond

Plants, animals, and other organisms live within every ecosystem. The living component of an ecosystem is referred to as a "community." A pond, for example, is an ecosystem in which a

COURTESY OF HENRY MILNE/© NSRC

This pond is home to a great diversity of organisms.

community of organisms, including blackworms, dragonflies, and *Lemna,* all interact among themselves and with their nonliving environment. (The members of each species in a community are called a "population.")

These damselfly nymphs eventually move out of the water, unless they become fish food first!

Within this pond ecosystem—and others—are many different habitats, or homes. Blackworms may live in the muddy fringes of the pond. This is where they find shelter. This is also where they find food. This is their habitat—the place where their needs are met.

Dragonflies and damselflies live the first part of their lives in their pond water habitat as nymphs. They eventually climb up plant stems, where they change into their adult form. Then the area above and around the pond becomes their habitat.

Other organisms that share this pond ecosystem may have different habitats. For example, *Lemna,* or duckweed, live on the water's surface, closer to the light from the sun. Crayfish, on the other hand, live at the bottom of the pond, scavenging for food that falls from upper layers.

This ball of dung, which is waste matter from another organism, provides a food supply for this beetle, appropriately named the "dung beetle."

The destruction of these trees greatly changes the nature of the ecosystems and habitats in this area.

Finding an Organism's Niche

Organisms within an ecosystem perform certain jobs that keep the ecosystem functioning. In a pond, for example, birds and frogs keep the number of insects in check by eating them. In a grassy pasture habitat, dung beetles may eat the waste matter from cows and other animals, which helps to recycle nutrients. These are their functions, their jobs—their niches.

Everything Changes

Don't think for a minute that ecosystems, habitats, communities, and populations don't change. They do. Ponds dry up. Forests are ravaged by fires. Hurricanes blow down trees. Organisms become extinct. These are all natural processes. However, change also occurs because of human intervention. A river gets dammed, creating a lake in the process. Grasslands get mowed and turned into soybean fields. Or trees get cut down and replaced by parking lots or housing developments.

All over the world, animals, plants, and other species come and go—and habitats and ecosystems shift and change over time. Change, in fact, is one thing we can always rely on. ☐

Wisconsin Fast Plants: Beginning the Cycle

Seeds can be beautifully arranged to appear as works of art!

KEITH WELLER, AGRICULTURAL RESEARCH SERVICE/UNITED STATES DEPARTMENT OF AGRICULTURE

INTRODUCTION

You will now begin the first in a series of activities to explore the life cycles of two organisms—Wisconsin Fast Plants *(Brassica rapa)* and the cabbage white butterfly *(Pieris rapae)*. Notice the similarity between their scientific names. This is no coincidence, as you will discover.

In this lesson, you will focus on Wisconsin Fast Plants. You will assemble a growing system in which to sow your seeds. You'll place your growing system in a plant light house that you will share with other groups. You will prepare a specific concentration of nutrient solution to fertilize your plants. You also will observe and document the germination of corn and lima bean seeds and their development into adult plants. Later in the module, you will use your developing Fast Plants to learn about important processes such as pollination, reproduction, heredity, transpiration, and photosynthesis.

OBJECTIVES FOR THIS LESSON

Prepare the equipment for the maintenance and development of the Wisconsin Fast Plants.

Sow the Wisconsin Fast Plants seeds in the growing system.

Examine the role of water and minerals in the growth and development of plants.

Become familiar with the life cycle of Wisconsin Fast Plants.

Document the germination and development of a corn seed and a lima bean seed.

Explore the similarities and differences between corn (monocot) and bean (dicot) seeds and plants.

Update the organism photo card for Wisconsin Fast Plants.

NUTRITIONAL NEEDS OF PLANTS

If you've ever seen a commercial for plant food, you might have the impression that plants depend on humans to supply their food. Actually, plants don't need us to feed them because they manufacture their own food called glucose. This "real" plant food is a simple form of sugar from which plants obtain energy. To be considered food, a substance must provide energy.

In addition to glucose, light, water, air, and a suitable temperature, plants need minerals to grow and develop. The Fast Plants that you will grow in class, as well as the African violet on your kitchen windowsill or the tomato plants in your garden, need a variety of miner-als. Unlike food, minerals do not supply plants with energy. However, without the proper minerals, plants will not function properly; they will not grow and thrive.

The truth is, the plant food sold in stores isn't really food at all because it doesn't contain an energy source. It's a mixture of substances that plants need for proper growth and development. Sometimes these mixtures are referred to as fertilizers, which is a more accurate term, because their purpose is to fertilize plants, or to enable them to grow and develop properly. When plants cannot get all of the minerals they need naturally, humans often step in to lend a hand.

(continued)

This beautiful African violet most likely receives the proper concentration of fertilizer and water.

Unused water evaporates through pores in leaves.

Root hairs provide more surface area for absorption of water and minerals.

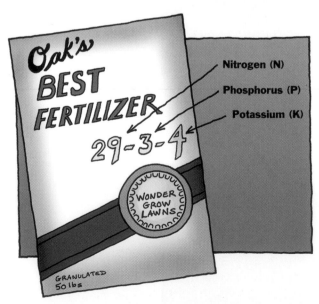

Nitrogen (N)

Phosphorus (P)

Potassium (K)

Do you think this lawn fertilizer would work effectively for houseplants, too?

How do these minerals enter the plants? Plants absorb them from the soil through their root systems.

Fertilizers to the Rescue

Some soil is rich and fertile. It can supply all the minerals that most plants need. But using soil over and over again can deplete the soil's natural mineral supply. Recycling organic materials such as grass and leaves is a good way to revitalize outdoor soil. Sometimes, however, even recycling isn't enough. In these cases, farmers and gardeners must add fertilizer that contains essential minerals. Eventually, a potted plant also will need fertilizer because its soil supply is limited.

There are many different types of fertilizer—for lawns, houseplants, and outdoor plants, for example. Each type contains the same basic nutrients, but in proportions that meet the specific needs of certain plants. Some mixtures help plants grow strong roots; others promote beautiful blossoms or huge fruit.

You can find much of the information you need about the minerals that a fertilizer supplies by reading its label, as you can see on the example to the left. For further details about these minerals, read on!

Macro and Micronutrients

Plants need a total of 13 different minerals. Of these, three are especially important because plants need them in greater quantities than they need the others. These "macronutrients" are nitrogen, phosphorus, and potassium. Notice that there is a line on the fertilizer label that says "29-3-4." This refers to the proportions, in order, of each of these three nutrients in the fertilizer. This lawn fertilizer, for example, contains 29 percent nitrogen.

Nitrogen promotes the growth of healthy leaves. It also contributes to overall plant health. A plant that does not get enough nitrogen will have light green leaves and thin stems. Its lower leaves will turn yellow and brown. Lawns need a great deal of nitrogen.

COURTESY POTASH & PHOSPHATE INSTITUTE, NORCROSS, GEORGIA

COURTESY POTASH & PHOSPHATE INSTITUTE, NORCROSS, GEORGIA

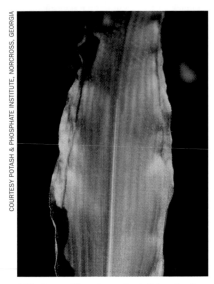

COURTESY POTASH & PHOSPHATE INSTITUTE, NORCROSS, GEORGIA

Which characteristics of a nitrogen-deprived plant appear in this photo?

How can you tell this plant needs phosphorus?

What are the signs that this plant needs potassium?

If a flowering plant gets too much nitrogen, its leaves will grow too much and flowering will slow.

The second macronutrient is phosphorus (called "phosphate" on the label). As the label indicates, this lawn fertilizer contains 3 percent phosphorus. Phosphorous promotes strong, healthy roots. It also helps flowers bloom. Bulb plants such as tulips need high amounts of phosphorus. So do newly transplanted trees and shrubs, which must establish a root system before they can start to grow again. Plants that do not get enough phosphorus do not grow well. Their leaves become too dark. The whole plant may turn purple-blue and leaves may drop off.

Potassium (called "potash" on the label) helps plants withstand dramatic temperature changes and protects them from disease. A plant that does not get enough potassium may have brown leaves that curve downward and droop. The lawn fertilizer has 4 percent potassium. Both potassium and phosphorus can be harmful in their most concentrated form. That's why they are placed in fertilizer in less-concentrated, less-harmful forms—potash and phosphate.

If the three most important minerals are known as macronutrients, what do you think the other 10 are called? Micronutrients! Of these 10 micronutrients, calcium, magnesium, and sulfur are usually the most important. For lawns, however, iron is an important mineral. The other micronutrients are boron, copper, chlorine, manganese, molybdenum, and zinc. Because plants need only very small amounts of these minerals, they also are called "trace elements."

Too Much of a Good Thing?

The proportions on the lawn fertilizer label are 29-3-4. The fertilizer you will use in this module is 20-20-20. It has equal proportions of the three macronutrients. That makes it a good all-purpose fertilizer.

When it comes to fertilizing, too little is sometimes better than too much. Too much fertilizer may cause poisonous mineral salts to build up in the soil and damage the roots. This can be fatal for plants. The actual strength of the fertilizer is determined by how much water is mixed with a given amount of fertilizer.

In this module, you will use a 12.5 percent concentration of 20-20-20 fertilizer, one that is most suitable for the growth and development of your Fast Plants.

Getting Started

1. With your group, agree on the function of a seed and write that function in your science notebook.

2. Develop a list of seeds you think are edible. Agree on why you think some seeds may be a good source of nutrition for humans.

3. Discuss your responses with the class.

MATERIALS FOR LESSON 5

For You
1 copy of Student Sheet 5.1: Fast Plants Maintenance Chart
1 pair of safety goggles

For your group
Materials for 1 Wisconsin Fast Plants growing system
1 pair of scissors
250 mL of stock fertilizer solution
1 soda bottle with cap, empty and clean
1 250-mL graduated cylinder
1 black marker
1 corn and bean growing system

Inquiry 5.1
Preparing Your Growing System

PROCEDURE

1. Working with your group, prepare your growing system in the following manner:

A. At the station your teacher has set up, use the flame to heat the tip of a dissecting needle until it is red hot, as seen in Figure 5.1.

B. Quickly push the needle through the center of the bottom of the small cup and work it around until it melts a hole. Reheat the needle's tip as necessary. Use the lines that form a small triangle at the center of the cup's bottom as the outer boundaries of the hole, as shown in Figure 5.2.

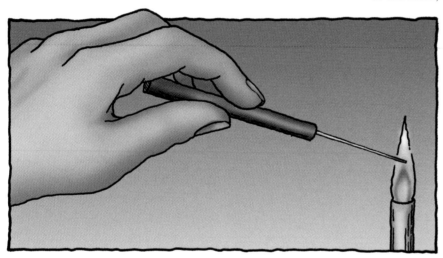

Figure 5.1 *Place only the tip of the dissecting needle in the flame.*

SAFETY TIPS

Always wear safety goggles when working around a flame.

Cool the hot needle with the water in the cup.

Figure 5.2 *The hole should be formed to the shape and size of the triangle at the center of the cup's bottom.*

C. Dip the needle in water to cool it. Back at your seat, use the tip of your dissecting needle to work the wick through the hole in the cup so you can pull it through, as shown in Figure 5.3.

D. Place the small cup (planter) into the large cup (reservoir). The wick should extend to the bottom of the large cup. Your growing system should look like the one shown in Figure 5.4.

2. Use the black marker to label the growing system "Fast Plants." Set the growing system aside while you conduct Inquiry 5.2.

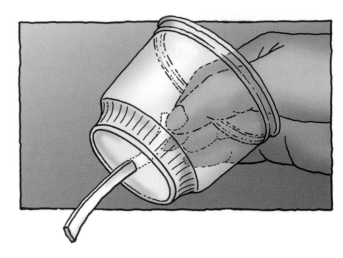

Figure 5.3 *Pull the wick through the bottom of the cup.*

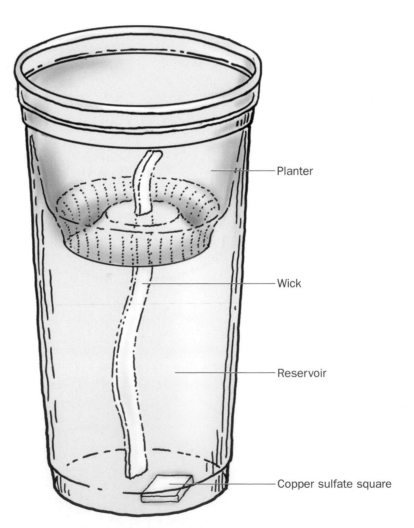

— Planter

— Wick

— Reservoir

— Copper sulfate square

Figure 5.4 *The proper position of the wick in the growing system*

Inquiry 5.2
Preparing Your Nutrient Solution

PROCEDURE

1. Discuss the reading selection "Nutritional Needs of Plants" with your class.

2. Use a graduated cylinder to measure 250 mL of stock fertilizer solution. Pour it into a 2-L plastic container.

3. Add tap water to the plastic container until it is almost full. Tighten its lid and shake the container to mix the nutrient solution.

4. Use your marker to label the container "12.5% Fertilizer Solution." Add your names and class period and keep the container handy to use for Inquiry 5.3.

Inquiry 5.3
Sowing the Fast Plants Seeds

PROCEDURE

1. Take the small cup (planter) out of the large cup (reservoir). While a group member holds the wick in the planter upright, add soil to it until it is full. Tap the bottom against the table to help settle the soil. Level off the excess soil so that it is even with the top of the cup. Place the planter back into the reservoir.

2. Gently soak the soil with nutrient solution. Let it seep through the soil until it begins to drip through the wick into the reservoir. This should cause the soil to shrink below the level of the rim.

3. Distribute eight Wisconsin Fast Plants seeds evenly around the perimeter of the planter, about 5 mm from the edge, as shown in Figure 5.5.

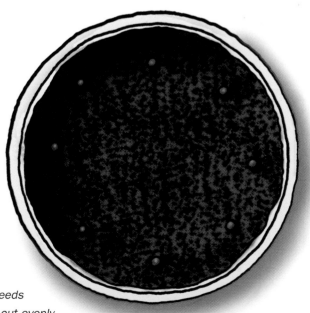

Figure 5.5 *Your seeds should be spread out evenly on the top of the soil.*

4. Cover the seeds with a thin layer of soil until the soil is level with the top of the planter.

5. Gently water the soil with your nutrient solution until it drips from the wick hanging down into the reservoir.

6. Use your black marker to place a mark on the outside of the reservoir cup just below the bottom of the planter. Remove the planter and add nutrient solution to that mark. Add a copper sulfate square to the reservoir to prevent the growth of algae. Replace the planter. Your growing system should now look like the one in Figure 5.6.

7. Make sure the light in your box is on. Then place your growing system inside and cover the front of the box with the aluminum foil curtain (see Figure 5.7).

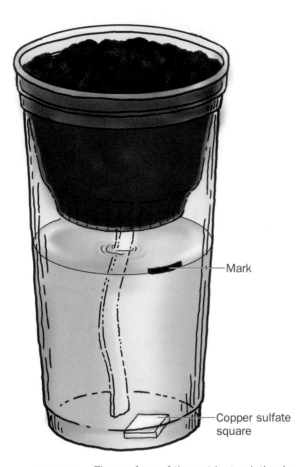

Figure 5.6 *The surface of the nutrient solution in the reservoir should be just below the bottom of the planter.*

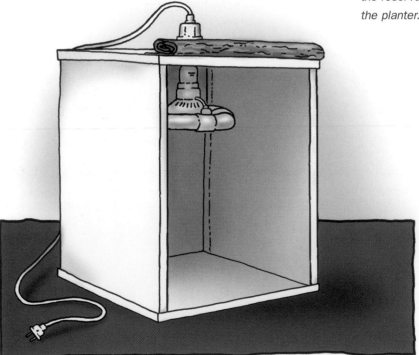

Figure 5.7 *Your plant light house*

Inquiry 5.4
Observing the Germination and Development of Corn and Bean Seeds

PROCEDURE

1. Observe the bean and corn seeds daily. As soon as the seeds begin to germinate, sketch the appearance of one bean and one corn seed in your science notebook. Use the reading selection "From Seed to Adult Plant—and Back" at the end of this lesson for help in labeling your germinating seeds.

2. If more than one corn seedling and one bean seedling emerge from the soil, remove the extras by cutting their stems at soil level.

3. Repeat your observations and sketches every 3 days for 2 weeks after germination.

4. After the 2-week period is over, list in your science notebook the similarities and differences between the two plants as they develop. Focus on seed structure, root structure, leaf structure, including the pattern of veins in the leaves. Be prepared to discuss your observations with the class.

5. At your teacher's direction, update your organism photo cards for the bean plant and for Wisconsin Fast Plants.

REFLECTING ON WHAT YOU'VE DONE

1. Refer to "Nutritional Needs of Plants" to answer the following questions in your science notebook:

A. How do water and minerals get into a plant?

B. What does "20-20-20" refer to on the fertilizer container label?

C. What could you do to affect the concentration of the nutrient solution?

2. Using the reader "Wisconsin Fast Plants: Sprouting Up All Over" as a reference, complete the following in your science notebook:

D. List at least three ways in which Wisconsin Fast Plants are special.

3. Refer to "From Seed to Adult Plant—and Back" to answer the following questions in your science notebook:

E. Where does the seed fit into the life cycle of the plant?

F. What is the difference between the cotyledons and the true leaves of flowering plants?

G. What structure develops to protect the seeds in flowering plants?

Wisconsin Fast Plants:
Sprouting Up All Over

If you ever visit the University of Wisconsin, do not overlook the Science House. It's a small building—the oldest wood-frame building on campus—built in 1868.

When you step inside Science House and talk with three people who work there, you will soon forget the other bigger and more modern buildings. You will learn a great deal. This is because Science House is where Wisconsin Fast Plants were born. Fast Plants have traveled from this house to research labs and classrooms all over the world. They've even traveled into space!

Why are the plants so special? Dr. Paul Williams, who developed them nearly 25 years ago, and program coordinators, Coe Williams

and Dan Lauffer, answer this question with enthusiasm.

From Seed to Seed in Just Six Weeks

The most important thing about Wisconsin Fast Plants is that they live up to their name. These small, yellow-flowered plants go through their life cycle in just over 6 weeks.

It wasn't always this way. Dr. Williams spent 15 years speeding up the plant's life cycle. He began with 2000 varieties of *Brassica* seeds gathered from around the world. He planted them in his lab, watered them, placed them under light, and watched them grow. From this first group, Dr. Williams selected seeds from the plants that had grown the fastest. He planted

The Fast Plants team at the University of Wisconsin includes (left to right) Coe Williams, Paul Williams, and Dan Lauffer.

those seeds and let them grow. Then he cross-pollinated the new plants. He continued this process, known as "selective breeding," for generation after generation. The plant's life cycle gradually shortened. Eventually, the life cycle of the selectively bred Fast Plant was 10 times shorter than it had been before Dr. Williams started his work.

Dr. Williams also was able to breed other qualities into the plants that make them useful for research. For example, the plants produce an above-average number of fertile seeds, don't need much space (in fact, they thrive in company), and grow best under constant light.

Smaller Can Be Better

Wisconsin Fast Plants were first distributed to classrooms in 1986, and they caught on quickly. Through the mail and a toll-free phone line, teachers and students began sharing their Fast Plants experiences with members of the Fast Plants team.

Teachers began reporting one problem: The plants grew fast, but they grew too large! The average height of a flowering plant was 20 centimeters. Teachers told Dr. Williams that the plants sometimes crept up into the light banks. Some were so tall that they flopped over.

Dr. Williams and the team decided to try to develop shorter plants with thicker stems. Again, the answer was selective breeding. Dr. Williams cross-pollinated Fast Plants that were shorter and had thicker stems than average. Several generations later, the average plant was only 15 centimeters high, and its life cycle was just as short as ever.

A Worldwide Network

Today, Fast Plants are distributed to scientists all over the world through a national network

COURTESY OF WISCONSIN FAST PLANTS

Paul Williams developed shorter Fast Plants (on left) through selective breeding.

called the Crucifer Genetic Cooperative. "Crucifers" are a family of plants that include Fast Plants, as well as cabbage, cauliflower, and Brussels sprouts. Crucifers, Dr. Williams says, will have great economic importance in the future, as the world's population increases and inexpensive, easy-to-grow sources of food are needed. The work being done with Fast Plants is laying a foundation for work with these related plants, which might be described as the Fast Plants' "cousins."

Sprouting in Space

If all this activity on Earth weren't enough, Fast Plants also have spent some time in space. In May 1997, the space shuttle *Atlantis* delivered a supply of Fast Plants seeds to the Russian space station Mir. The space team on board Mir included both American and Russian astronauts. Their job was to plant the seeds and see whether they would germinate, grow, flower, and produce seeds in microgravity, a nearly weightless environment. The name of this experiment was Greenhouse-3.

If plants that grow quickly were grown in outer space, they could provide a food source and a continuing supply of oxygen for astronauts.

The seeds were planted. They took about the same time to germinate in space as they did on Earth. American astronaut Mike Foale pollinated the plants by hand. So far, so good. Soon after, however, there was a collision between Mir and one of its supply ships. The space module that housed the tiny plants was in darkness for three days. Would the plants survive and produce new seeds? They did. When Mike Foale shined a flashlight on the seed pods, he could see the seeds inside. Power was restored to Mir, and the space capsule brought its precious cargo of new seeds back to Earth. The "space seeds" were planted, and a few months later, scientists verified that the seeds had germinated.

Why was the Mir experiment important? There are many reasons, according to Dr. Mary Musgrave, coordinator of the project. First, space scientists are looking for small plants that grow fast and that could be a healthy source of fresh food for astronauts. If plants could be grown on extended missions in space modules, Dr. Musgrave adds, they could help clean the air and generate oxygen as well. □

Dr. Mary Musgrave trains Commander Kevin Kriegel to pollinate Wisconsin Fast Plants.

From Seed to Adult Plant—and Back

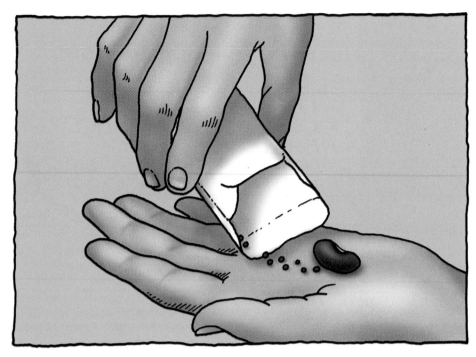

These tiny Wisconsin Fast Plants seeds look rather insignificant compared to this bean seed. But the plants that result from each type of seed are quite impressive, not to mention nutritious.

Take a look at some Fast Plants seeds. They are so tiny! They're hard and appear to be dry. In fact, they don't even look like they are alive. How does one of these small seeds turn into a plant?

The process by which a seed becomes a plant is called "germination." Because germination normally takes place underground, we do not see it happen. All we see is the exciting result—a tiny green plant emerging from the soil.

But suppose you had x-ray vision and could follow each step of what happens underneath the soil as a seed germinates. Here is what you would see.

Right after planting, a bean seed would look pretty much like it did before you placed it in the soil. That's because the seed is in a dor-

mant—or inactive—stage. Protected by its tough seed coat, the seed can withstand extremely hot and cold temperatures. Some varieties of seeds can remain dormant for years.

A dormant seed may look lifeless, but inside, it's a different story. Inside the seed is an embryo, which contains the tiny beginnings of a root, a stem, and leaves. These will become the major parts of the mature plant. An important food-storing tissue called "endosperm" surrounds the embryo. Also contained in the seed are one or more seed leaves, called "cotyledons." The seeds of some plants only have one cotyledon. These plants are called "monocotyledons," or monocots for short. Other plants, whose seeds contain two cotyledons, are called "dicotyledons," or dicots.

(continued)

Monocot seeds, which include cereal grains, wheat, rice, and corn, use energy from the endosperm to nourish the developing embryo and germinating seedling. Their cotyledon never emerges from the soil. Dicot seeds, such as bean and Fast Plants seeds, transfer energy from the endosperm to the cotyledons. These cotyledons emerge from the soil with the stem and continue to provide energy for the developing plant.

After the bean seed has been underground for a while, it begins to absorb water and gets larger. This happens faster when the ground is warm.

Finally, the process of germination begins. A root emerges from the seed. This root, called the "primary root," grows downward. It forms an anchor for the developing plant. Tiny root hairs and secondary roots form. Root hairs are microscopic, fingerlike extensions of the outer cells of the roots that give the root more surface area through which water and minerals may enter the plant.

Meanwhile, there is further activity in the seed. Water, which comes in through the root hairs, causes the tightly packed cells in the tiny young stem to elongate. This causes the stem to push upward. The cotyledons, which are at the top of the stem, are dragged upward through the soil until they poke through its surface. As the seed leaves sense light, they expand.

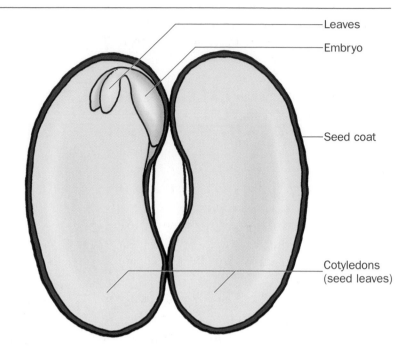

Leaves
Embryo
Seed coat
Cotyledons (seed leaves)

Notice the seed coat, cotyledons, and embryo of this bean seed.

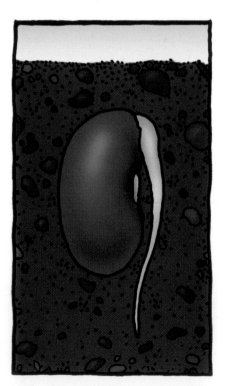

No matter what position the seed is in, the roots will still grow downward.

In bean plants, the cotyledons provide the energy for germination and emergence from the soil. As soon as the true leaves form and begin to function, the cotyledons wither and die. In Fast Plants, the cotyledons also supply energy for germination and emergence, but upon emergence, they expand, turn green, and gather energy from the sun for further growth until true leaves form to take on that role.

As the bean plant grows, it develops more leaves and its root system matures. The plant now is able to get the nutrients it needs from the soil, water, and air. It can also manufacture its own food in its leaves in a process called photosynthesis.

The plant eventually matures and flowers. The flowers are pollinated, fertilization occurs, and seeds develop. As the flowers wither, a fruit develops. The fruit provides a protective covering, which supports the development of the seeds, and aids in their dispersal. When these fruits decay, their seeds are left behind. Many are eaten by animals; some mold. But others survive, and given proper conditions, will germinate and grow—and the life cycle begins again. □

Three stages in the development of a young bean plant

If you plant a seed and it does not germinate, what could be the reason? Sometimes, when the soil is over-watered, the seed does not get enough oxygen. Occasionally, a seed doesn't germinate because it is too cold or it doesn't get enough water. More often than not, though, if a seed does not germinate, a fungus is the culprit, as you can see in this photograph.

© 1998 WILLY A. VERHEULPEN

The bean plant is looking more like an adult each day.

Soon, the seeds will fall from the ripened seed pods and the cycle will begin again.

Table 5.1 Wisconsin Fast Plants Maintenance Chart

Directions This table gives directions for tasks that your group must perform during the development of your Fast Plants in addition to ensuring that the plants receive a constant supply of light and nutrient solution.

Day 1 Sow Fast Plants seeds.	**2**	**3**	**4** Plants should have sprouted. If not, start over.	**5**	**6**
7 Thin growing system to six plants.	**8**	**9** Flower buds begin to appear.	**10**	**11**	**12**
13 Begin pollinating Fast Plants flowers.	**14** Continue pollinating flowers.	**15** Continue pollinating flowers.	**16** Continue pollinating flowers.	**17** Last day for pollinating flowers. Cut off unopened buds.	**18**
19	**20**	**21**	**22**	**23**	**24**
25	**26**	**27**	**28**	**29**	**30**
31	**32**	**33**	**34**	**35** Remove nutrient solution from reservoirs.	**36**
37	**38**	**39**	**40** Harvest your seeds. Set them up for germination.	**41**	**42**
43 Observe the stem and leaf color of the growing sprouts.	**44**	**45**	**46**	**47**	**48**

The Cabbage White— From Egg to Butterfly

COURTESY OF WISCONSIN FAST PLANTS

A butterfly emerges from its protective chrysalis.

INTRODUCTION

You have planted your Wisconsin Fast Plants seeds. Now it is time to begin to follow the life cycle of another organism, *Pieris rapae,* commonly known as the cabbage white butterfly. In the first inquiry of this lesson, you will observe, draw, and measure an egg and a newly hatched larva of a cabbage white butterfly. You will measure the body length of a larva every 3 days for 3 weeks to discover when the greatest growth in length occurs. In the second inquiry, you will explore the general food preferences of a cabbage white butterfly larva. In the third inquiry, you will look into whether adult cabbage white butterflies are attracted to one food color over another. After each inquiry, you will update your group's organism photo card for the cabbage white butterfly.

OBJECTIVES FOR THIS LESSON

Explain the meaning of the word *"Lepidoptera,"* the order of insects to which butterflies and moths belong.

Explain the life cycle stages of the cabbage white butterfly.

Measure the length of an egg and the length of the body of a newly hatched cabbage white butterfly larva.

Measure and record the body length of a cabbage white larva every 3 days for 3 weeks.

Observe the food preferences of a cabbage white butterfly larva.

Determine whether adult cabbage whites prefer one color of food over another.

Investigate the basic anatomy of an adult cabbage white butterfly.

Update the organism photo card for the cabbage white butterfly.

Inquiry 6.1
Observing and Measuring a Cabbage White Butterfly Egg and Larva

INTRODUCING THE CABBAGE WHITE BUTTERFLY

The cabbage white butterfly, like all butterflies, is an arthropod, which is an organism with jointed legs and a durable, protective body covering called an exoskeleton. Like the WOWBug and all other members of the class of arthropods called insects, the adult cabbage white has six legs, two antennae, two pairs of wings, and three main body parts—head, thorax, and abdomen.

The order of insects to which the cabbage white belongs is *Lepidoptera*. This name is formed from the Greek words *"lepid,"* which means scale, and *"ptera,"* which means wing. Some scientists believe the word "butterfly" comes from England's Brimstone butterfly, whose name is thought to be a contraction of "butter-covered fly."

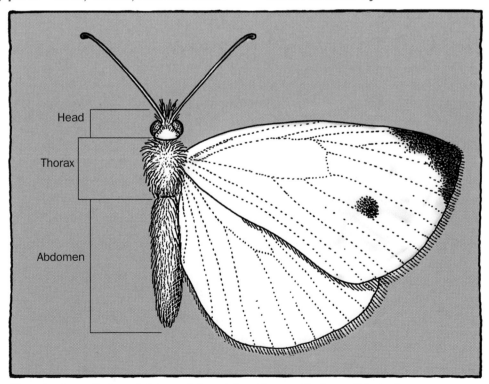

Note the three distinct divisions of the adult cabbage white butterfly's body.

MATERIALS FOR INQUIRY 6.1

For you

1 copy of Student Sheet 6.1A: Template for Drawings of Cabbage White Egg and Larva

1 copy of Student Sheet 6.1B: Tracking the Growth of a Cabbage White Larva

1 copy of Inquiry Master 6.1B: Cabbage White Butterfly—Inquiry, Care, and Maintenance Calendar

For your group

1 set of organism photo cards

2 20-egg, waxed paper strips

2 compound light microscopes

2 plastic slides

2 transparent rulers

2 hand lenses

2 petri dish bottoms

1 black marker

2 dissecting needles

2 metric rulers, 30 cm (12 in.)

Getting Started

1. In your science notebook, list three things that you know about butterflies.

2. With your class, read "Introducing the Cabbage White Butterfly" at the beginning of this inquiry. Add new information to your list.

3. Discuss your list with the class, and add new information shared by your classmates.

PROCEDURE

1. Working with your partner, place a waxed paper strip into a petri dish with the side holding the cabbage white eggs facing up. Place the petri dish on the microscope stage.

2. Locate and focus on an egg under 40×; then switch to 100× and refocus.

Figure 6.1 *This leaf contains both eggs and newly hatched larvae. Can you guess what caused the holes in the leaf?*

3. Draw the egg in the top circle on Student Sheet 6.1A: Template for Drawings of Cabbage White Egg and Larva. Refer to Student Sheet 2.3A: Guidelines for Scientific Drawings for a reminder of where to put the magnification and title on your drawing.

4. Observe and draw a newly hatched larva by taking the following steps:

A. While looking into the eyepiece of the microscope, slowly move the petri dish until you see a larva, which is a tiny caterpillar.

B. Switch to the highest magnification that will keep the entire larva in the field of view.

C. Draw the larva in the lower circle on Student Sheet 6.1A. Label any features of the larva that you can identify.

5. Follow these steps to measure and record the larva's body length:

A. Place the transparent ruler next to a larva on the waxed paper strip. Avoid placing the ruler on the eggs.

B. Observe the ruler and the larva through the microscope. Position the ruler so that one end of the larva is in the center of one of the lines on the ruler, in the same manner that you measured the WOWBug in Lesson 2 (see Figure 2.6).

C. Record the length of the larva in parentheses to the right of the title of your drawing. Put the transparent ruler back into the plastic box.

D. Record your information on Student Sheet 6.1B: Tracking the Growth of a Cabbage White Larva. Be sure to note today's date in the first column. In the last column, list features and behaviors of the larva that you can observe.

COURTESY OF CAROLINA BIOLOGICAL SUPPLY COMPANY

Figure 6.2 *This is one of the granddaddies of all caterpillars, the larva of the Polyphemus moth.*

6. The last group that works with the waxed paper strip should lay the strip on a leaf of the radish growing system. Use your marker to label the growing system with your group number (assigned by your teacher) and place it in the butterfly light house. All groups sharing a plant light house, including your group, will be responsible for the care and maintenance of this growing system as well as that of your Fast Plants.

7. Discuss with your group the things you have learned about the cabbage white butterfly. List these things on your group's organism photo card for the cabbage white. Erase or revise any information on the card that you have learned is incorrect. Return the card to your teacher.

8. Have your group members take turns making the measurement of larval body length every 3 days for 3 weeks, recording it each time on Student Sheet 6.1B and sharing the information with the group.

9. Predict the time period during which the greatest growth in length of the larva will

occur. Explain your choice. Record it on Table 1 on Student Sheet 6.1B.

10. When you have completed Table 1, graph your results on the same student sheet.

REFLECTING ON WHAT YOU'VE DONE

Answer the following questions on Student Sheet 6.1A:

A. List the three main body parts of an adult butterfly. If necessary, refer to the reading selection "Introducing the Cabbage White Butterfly" at the beginning of this lesson.

B. Did you see all three insect body parts in the larva? Explain.

C. According to the maintenance calendar on Inquiry Master 6.1B: Cabbage White Butterfly—Inquiry, Care, and Maintenance Calendar, approximately how many days is it from the time the egg hatches until an adult butterfly emerges from its chrysalis?

Inquiry 6.2
Food Preferences of a Cabbage White Butterfly Larva

WHAT DO CABBAGE WHITE BUTTERFLY LARVAE LIKE TO EAT?

You have probably noticed that the leaves of the radish plants on which you put the butterfly eggs are not in very good shape. This is because when a larva hatches from an egg it becomes an eating machine—immediately crawling up the plant stems to reach the leaves.

The larva constantly eats, grows, excretes, and molts. Molting, or the shedding of the outer skin, is necessary because the outer skin (exoskeleton) that covers and protects the larva does not grow. As the larva increases in size, the outer skin cracks to reveal a baggy inner skin. Then the larva crawls out of its outer skin and resumes eating. The more it eats, the larger it grows. The larger it grows, the more it eats. The larva undergoes four molts before it reaches full size.

The droppings of the larva, called "frass," first appear as tiny pellets on the leaves of the plants on which the larva feeds. The frass consists of the parts of the plant tissue that the larva does not digest and use.

You already know that the larva will eat the radish leaves. The radish is a member of the mustard, or cabbage, family. Given a choice, would the larva eat the leaves of a plant from a different plant family? You'll find out when you design and carry out an inquiry to answer these questions. Allow time during your inquiry to observe the composition of a piece of frass.

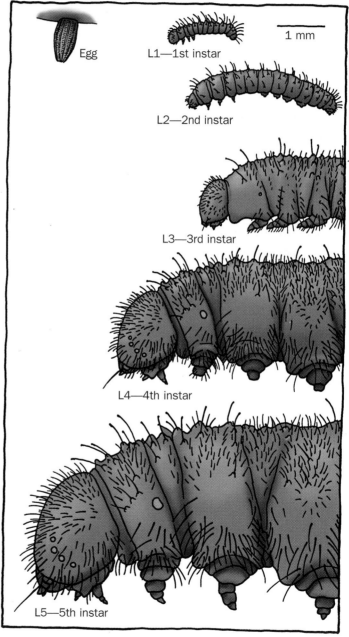

Egg

L1—1st instar

1 mm

L2—2nd instar

L3—3rd instar

L4—4th instar

L5—5th instar

There are five stages, or instars, in the development of the cabbage white butterfly larva.

MATERIALS FOR INQUIRY 6.2

For You

1 copy of Student
  Sheet 6.2: Larva
  Food Preferences

For your group

1 set of organism
  photo cards
1 cabbage white
  butterfly larva
1 Fast Plants leaf
1 lettuce leaf
1 spinach leaf
1 petri dish
1 piece of filter
  paper
2 cotton swabs
2 compound light
  microscopes
2 plastic slides
2 coverslips
2 dissecting needles
2 plastic pipettes
1 pair of scissors
  Tap water

Getting Started

1. List three of your favorite foods in your science notebook. Below your list, explain why you like these particular foods.

2. Discuss your responses with the class.

PROCEDURE

1. Listen while a classmate reads aloud "What Do Cabbage White Butterfly Larvae Like To Eat?" Ask questions to clarify any points you do not understand.

2. Discuss with your group how to set up an inquiry to find out which leaf or leaves a cabbage white larva will eat. You may use the materials in the materials list. If you need additional lab materials, ask your teacher if they are available. When designing your inquiry, consider factors such as—

- how to ensure that all the plants have an equal chance of being eaten by the larva
- what specific behaviors you will observe that will tell you which plant the larva prefers
- what things (variables) you will keep the same in your inquiry

3. Share your ideas with the class.

4. Based on the class discussion, work with your group to revise your inquiry design. On Student Sheet 6.2, list the steps you will take to conduct your inquiry. Then design a chart or data table on which to record your observations. When you have completed your inquiry design, proceed to Step 5.

5. Pick up the materials you need to conduct your inquiry. To transfer a larva from a radish plant to your petri dish, follow these steps:

A. Place a piece of filter paper in the lid of a petri dish.

B. Hold one end of a cotton swab while you place the other end lengthwise against the larva. Then, slowly and gently turn the swab counterclockwise so that it burrows under the larva and lifts it without hurting it, as shown in Figure 6.3.

C. Reverse Procedure B to set the larva in the petri dish. You may need to use the tip of your dissecting needle to nudge the larva away from the cotton swab. Be careful; even a tiny puncture of the larva's exoskeleton can kill it.

6. While you are waiting for the larva to make its food choice, have one pair in your group continue to watch it, while the other pair moves on to Step 8. Switch responsibilities when the first pair has completed Step 9.

Figure 6.3 *Slowly and gently lift the larva from the plant using the cotton swab.*

COURTESY OF HENRY MILNE/© NSRC

Figure 6.4 *This student is looking closely at the larva she picked up with a cotton swab.*

7. Observe the difference in the color of the frass left by the larva in the petri dish and on the radish plant. Notice the color of the frass in Figure 6.5.

8. Use your dissecting needle to transfer one piece of frass to a microscope slide. Add a drop of water using a plastic pipette. Mash the frass with the needle, and mix it with the water. Add a coverslip. Observe the mashed frass with your microscope under 100× magnification, then under 400×. Discuss with your group what you have observed.

9. When you have finished the inquiry, have one group member use the cotton swab to return the larva to a leaf of the radish plant.

10. Have another student rinse and dry the slide and coverslip. Have everyone wash his or her hands.

11. With your group, update your organism photo card for the cabbage white butterfly.

COURTESY OF WISCONSIN FAST PLANTS

Figure 6.5 *As the larvae feed on this head of cabbage, the frass accumulates in piles on the paper. What do you think the frass would look like if this were purple cabbage?*

REFLECTING ON WHAT YOU'VE DONE

Answer the following questions on Student Sheet 6.2:

A. Which species of leaf did the larva eat? How does this choice relate to where the butterfly lays its eggs?

B. What did you observe in the frass of the butterfly larva? Explain.

C. Refer to the reading selection "Picky Eaters" and list at least two factors that influence how insects choose their diets.

SAFETY TIP

Wash your hands thoroughly with soap and water after handling the frass of the butterfly larva.

PICKY EATERS

Do you love corn but hate broccoli? Can't get enough potatoes but turn up your nose at cabbage? If so, you've got something in common with insects. Like many humans, insects can be picky eaters.

How does an insect recognize a leaf, a fruit, or a vegetable as food? And how does it decide whether that particular leaf or vegetable might be a great dinner? The answers vary—depending on the insect. But all insects determine what they will eat by responding to specific cues.

This cabbage white larva can devour this leaf in a matter of minutes! Can you guess what the larva finds so attractive about this leaf?

About half of all insects depend on plants to survive. What do they look for in a diet? For them, odor and taste are the most important cues. These odor and taste cues are generated by chemicals in plants.

Plants in the *Brassicaceae* (often called *Cruciferae),* or mustard, family, for example, are characterized by a sharp, strong odor and flavor. The strong taste and smell are caused by mustard oils and chemicals called glucosides. The *Brassicaceae* is one of the most important groups of vegetable crops and include radishes, mustard greens, turnips, watercress, cabbage, cauliflower, broccoli, and Brussels sprouts. Many insects (and many people) won't eat these plants because of the way they smell or taste.

Entomologists have learned that chemicals such as glucosides have nothing to do with a plant's growth or metabolism. Their main job seems to be to make the plant unappetizing to the typical hungry, plant-eating insect. The scientists call glucosides and similar chemicals "secondary substances."

But a plant's chemical defense mechanism doesn't deter some insects. Some types of moths, flies, beetles, and aphids thrive on the mustard oils that other insects find so distasteful. The cabbage plant alone, despite its strong-smelling chemical oils, attracts more than 25 different kinds of pests. These pests eat only plants that contain mustard oils and glucosides.

Farmers and gardeners depend on entomologists to help them understand insect feeding habits. It's an important area of study; in fact, more than half of all entomologists are engaged in this type of work. The more they learn about insects' feeding cues, the more farmers will be able to harvest healthy crops. Then you—not the insects—will be able to enjoy a healthy dinner or snack!

(continued)

Examples of the many members of the mustard family

Broccoli and cauliflower

Purple cabbage

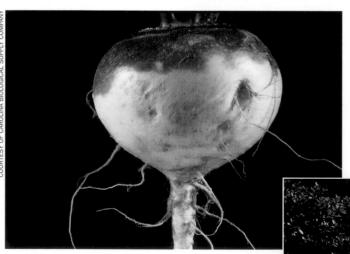

Green cabbage

Turnip

Ornamental cabbages

Inquiry 6.3
Exploring Food Color Preferences of the Cabbage White Butterfly

IS COLOR A FACTOR IN ATTRACTING CABBAGE WHITES TO A FOOD SOURCE?

The sugar, water, minerals, and other nutrients found in the nectar of flowers are the main sources of food for cabbage white butterflies. Nectar provides the energy they need during their quest for mates and for suitable plants on which to lay their eggs. Without it, the butterflies die within a few days.

You've probably noticed the adult butterflies feeding on the liquid mixture in the butterfly house. If you observe closely, you can see how the proboscis, the mouth part of an adult butterfly, takes in nutrients and water. The butterfly's proboscis is an elongated feeding tube that can be coiled or extended through the use of special muscles. The length of the proboscis varies greatly, depending on the butterfly species and on the particular flowers that serve as its primary food source. Can you estimate the length of an adult cabbage white's proboscis?

In Inquiry 6.2, you gave a cabbage white larva a choice of three green leaves, one of which was

A cabbage white butterfly is perched and ready to feed on the nectar of a Fast Plants flower.

The cabbage white enjoys a meal the only way it can—with its proboscis extended.

from a Fast Plant—a member of the mustard, or cabbage, family. You probably found that the larva ate only the Fast Plants leaf. Since all three leaves were green, you could not know whether color was a factor in attracting the larva to a specific leaf.

Each butterfly house has two feeders. Each contains the same sugar-honey-water mixture; however, each feeder contains a different vegetable coloring—one red, one blue, one green, and one yellow. Since adult cabbage whites cannot break down the food coloring in their digestive systems, their droppings will be the same color as the mixture they eat. In this inquiry, you will use a photocopy of paper that lined the bottom of a butterfly house with four feeders in it—one of each color. You will discover if color is a factor in attracting a cabbage white butterfly to its food.

This butterfly proboscis is coiled into its resting position.

MATERIALS FOR INQUIRY 6.3

For You
- 1 copy of Student Sheet 6.3: Food Color Preference Data Sheet

For your group
- 1 set of organism photo cards
- 1 photocopy of butterfly droppings
- 1 metric ruler, 30 cm (12 in.)
- 1 black marker

Getting Started

1. In Inquiry 6.2 you discovered that odor and taste are two elements that attract insects to certain foods. Discuss with your group whether color might also be a factor. Explain why in your science notebook.

2. Discuss your responses with the class.

PROCEDURE

1. Listen while your classmates take turns reading aloud "Is Color a Factor in Attracting Cabbage Whites to a Food Source?" Ask questions to clear up anything you do not understand.

2. Based on the reading selection, brainstorm with your group how to use the photocopy of butterfly droppings to determine whether color is a factor in attracting adult cabbage whites to their food.

3. Discuss your ideas with the class.

4. With your group, predict which color of drop you will find most often on the photocopy. Record your prediction on Student Sheet 6.3 and explain why your group chose this color.

5. Agree on the best way to divide up the task of counting the drops on the photocopy of butterfly droppings and determining whether color is a factor in attracting adult cabbage whites to their food.

6. Conduct the inquiry with your group. Record your data on Student Sheet 6.3.

7. When all groups in your class have finished, follow your teacher's directions for sharing your information.

8. Update your organism photo card for the cabbage white butterfly.

REFLECTING ON WHAT YOU'VE DONE

Answer the following questions on Student Sheet 6.3:

The painted lady is another species widely studied in elementary and middle schools.

A. According to your data, did the butterflies prefer one color of nectar over another? If so, which color?

B. Did the photocopy of the butterfly droppings have any color of drops other than the original four colors? Explain why you think this happened.

C. What factors involved in the setup of the feeders and butterfly house do you think needed to be controlled in the preparation of the paper with the different colors of drops?

D. Refer to the reading selection "The Delicate Balance of Life" at the end of this lesson to learn about other organisms that depend on a specific type of food for survival. Explain how an organism's limited diet narrows down its habitat choices.

The Delicate Balance of Life

A specialized diet can confine organisms to specific habitats. Take the giant panda, whose main food is bamboo. Its restricted diet limits its choice of habitats to places where bamboo forests grow—in remote, mountainous areas of China. Occasionally, there are shortages of bamboo, and some pandas starve.

Wouldn't more food choices help ensure survival? You bet. Consider the cabbage white butterfly. Its larvae feed on the leaves of cabbage, broccoli, kale, cauliflower, and other vegetables in the mustard family. With so many food choices, cabbage white butterflies roam freely across North America. However, specializing in cabbage won't help in an area such as a desert, where there are no cabbage plants.

In areas where the butterflies have plenty of food, some farmers consider them pests. They

JESSIE COHEN, SMITHSONIAN NATIONAL ZOO

Home is where the food is.

The cabbage white probably wouldn't choose this environment for its home. Why? There's nothing for them to eat!

sometimes use mint oil and other substances to destroy the larvae. Birds, snakes, and parasitic wasps that attack the larvae and pupae also help keep the butterflies in check. Balance is maintained because the butterflies have lots of food choices, and, unfortunately for them, so do their enemies!

What happens when an animal eats everything but nothing eats it? That's exactly what happened on Guam. About 50 years ago, brown tree snakes from Australia and New Guinea got aboard ships that eventually docked at this island in the Pacific Ocean. The snakes escaped onto the island. Because they had no natural predators on Guam, the snakes soon upset the island's natural balance. They fed on birds, bats, and lizards—animals that had never lived with such predators, and so had few natural defenses against them.

In time, many of these native animals vanished from the island. Then the snakes were forced to look for other food—in people's homes. Needless to say, this was rather upsetting to the islanders' home life! ☐

Few organisms are safe from this predator, the dreaded brown tree snake.

GYPSY MOTHS
From Invited Guests to Major Pests

Poor gypsy moths! Unlike butterflies, everybody hates them. People spray insecticides on their trees to kill them. They burn gypsy moth eggs and they drown gypsy moth caterpillars. Is that any way to treat a guest?

After all, gypsy moths were brought to the United States around 1870—on purpose! An amateur scientist named Etienne Leopold Trouvelot brought them, hoping to create a new type of silkworm, a caterpillar that produces silk cocoons. Unfortunately, the experiment failed and some of the caterpillars escaped from Trouvelot's Massachusetts home.

Efforts to control the escapees didn't work. Because their food preferences were diverse, the gypsies found plenty to eat. Luckily for them, they found few enemies. Their numbers swelled, and now this one-time guest is a major pest in the northeastern United States and southeastern Canada. Gypsy moths have devoured tree leaves and laid waste to forests for more than a century.

Metamorphosis

Like butterflies and other moths, gypsy moths transform themselves as they develop, during a process known as "metamorphosis." In the spring, they hatch from eggs as caterpillars. The caterpillars grow and molt several times before encasing themselves in cocoons. Finally, they emerge as winged insects. It's during the caterpillar, or larval, stage that gypsy moths do most of their serious eating—and damage.

Destroyer

Unlike the rather finicky cabbage white caterpillars, gypsy moth larvae

Everybody hates the poor gypsy moth.

are much less fussy eaters. They feast on apple, alder, birch, maple, poplar, and willow—500 species in all! Gypsies come into an area like a plague. Each one eats only a couple of leaves a day, but together, a group of gypsy moths can consume the leaves of a wooded tract hundreds of kilometers long in less than 3 months! When a tree is stripped of its leaves, it becomes weak. After several attacks by the gypsies, most trees die.

Misguided Control Efforts

A fly that preys on the gypsy moth was brought to the United States from Europe in an effort to control its spread. Unfortunately, studies show that this fly is killing more than gypsy moths. It is also feeding on several species of giant silk moths. Because of this fly, the large *Cecropia* moth, which has a wingspan of up to 15 centimeters, is declining in number. These findings led to the abandonment of this fly as a biological control in 1986, after decades of use in as many as 30 states. Unfortunately, the fly is still well established in many areas.

Most scientists believe that before a new species is introduced into an ecosystem, thorough studies of the possible consequences should be conducted. What's the point of getting rid of one pest if you're just going to have another? ☐

It won't take long for this gypsy moth larva to devour this leaf.

Gypsy moth larvae can devastate a forest by stripping the trees of their leaves.

Should we have risked endangering this beautiful Cecropia *moth* by bringing in one species to rid us of another?

Exploring Cells

When Robert Hooke first looked at a slice of cork through a microscope, the "tiny cavities" he described reminded him of a bee's honeycomb. It prompted him to call the tiny cavities cells.

COURTESY OF CAROLINA BIOLOGICAL SUPPLY COMPANY

INTRODUCTION

In Lessons 1 through 6, you looked briefly at many of the organisms that you will explore in more depth in the rest of this module. To learn more about organisms, you must first understand the nature of the cell, which is the basic unit of life. In this lesson, you will observe algal, plant, and animal cells through a microscope. You will draw, label, and measure the cells, following the guidelines for scientific drawings. You also will compare the structures of the cells and discuss whether their structures are suited to their functions.

OBJECTIVES FOR THIS LESSON

Observe, draw, label, and measure cells based on specific guidelines.

Observe and identify certain organelles of plant and animal cells.

Observe the effect of salt solution on *Elodea* leaf cells.

Compare the structure of various cells for evidence that they are suited to their functions.

Update the organism photo cards for *Elodea, Spirogyra,* and humans.

PLANT AND ANIMAL CELLS: THE SAME, BUT DIFFERENT

Almost all living things on Earth are made up of cells. Cells are the basic units of life. The simplest organisms—amoebae, for example—consist of only one cell. Complex organisms, such as humans, have trillions of cells that are divided into about 200 different types. Each cell type has a different function.

As the building blocks of living matter, plant and animal cells have many things in common. They also differ in some ways. Those differences are important because they point to some of the factors that distinguish one form of life from another. To understand this better,

let's take a cross-sectional look at an animal cell and a plant cell.

Inside an Animal Cell

Although there is no typical animal cell, most animal cells have three basic parts that scientists call "cellular organelles." Organelle means "little organ." The first organelle is the cell membrane, sometimes referred to as the "plasma membrane." This living membrane separates the cell from the rest of its environment and helps control the passage of substances into and out of the cell.

(continued)

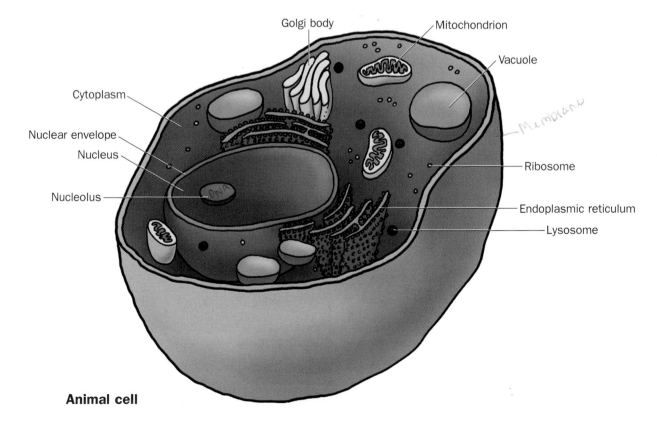

Animal cell

(continued from pg. 83)

The second cellular organelle is the "nucleus," which usually occupies the central portion of the animal cell. Think of the nucleus as "command central." The nucleus regulates all the activities that take place in the cell. Instructions for the cell's activities are stored in the chromosomes, which are found in the nucleus. The chromosomes, which almost always occur in pairs, are composed of a substance called "DNA" (deoxyribonucleic acid). DNA carries the hereditary traits that are passed from parent to offspring. The nucleus is surrounded by a double membrane called the "nuclear envelope."

The third basic cellular organelle is a jelly-like substance called "cytoplasm," which lies between the cell membrane and the nuclear envelope. In addition to the three basic cellular organelles, there are additional organelles in the cytoplasm. Each organelle carries out a specific cell function. For example, nutrients are broken down in the sausage-shaped organelles called "mitochondria." The energy produced in these organelles is either released to support the cell's activities or stored in the cell for future use. That is why mitochondria are often referred to as the "powerhouses" of the cell.

Ribosomes are organelles that help make the proteins that the cell needs to perform its life activities. Many ribosomes are located along the endoplasmic reticulum, or ER for short. The ER is a series of cavities that is connected to the nuclear envelope. Some substances travel between the nucleus and cytoplasm through these cavities. Golgi bodies package the proteins made by the ribosomes so that they can be sent out of the cell. Organelles called "lysosomes" help the cell digest proteins. The cytoplasm also contains organelles called vacuoles. Filled with water, food, or waste, they are the cell's "storage tanks."

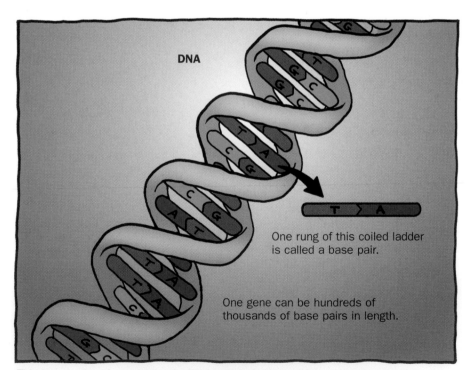

DNA

One rung of this coiled ladder is called a base pair.

One gene can be hundreds of thousands of base pairs in length.

This is a model of a portion of a DNA molecule that makes up a chromosome. Hereditary structures called genes are made up of varying numbers of base pairs.

Inside a Plant Cell

Plant and animal cells have the same basic cell parts—cell membrane, nucleus, and cytoplasm. But there are some differences.

First, the plant cell is surrounded by a rigid, outer layer called the "cell wall." The cell wall contains cellulose, a tough substance that supports and protects the cell. Like the cell membrane that lies within, the cell wall allows materials to pass into and out of the cell. Unlike the cell membrane, the cell wall is nonliving.

The nucleus is much the same in plant and animal cells. But some of the organelles in the plant cell's cytoplasm are different. For example, some plant cells have organelles called "plastids," which contain pigments. Pigments give parts of plants their characteristic colors—

red for tomatoes, orange for carrots, and green for spinach.

A chloroplast is a special plastid in a plant's leaf and stem cells. Chloroplasts contain a green pigment called chlorophyll. Chlorophyll traps energy from the sun. Plant cells use this energy to produce glucose, a simple sugar, during a process called photosynthesis. The vacuoles in plant cells are much larger than those in animal cells. Most plants have a large central vacuole that helps support the plant cell and also serves as a storage place for water, sugar, starch, and protein.

Although plant and animal cells have many organelles in common, each has organelles that the other does not, making them the same, but different!

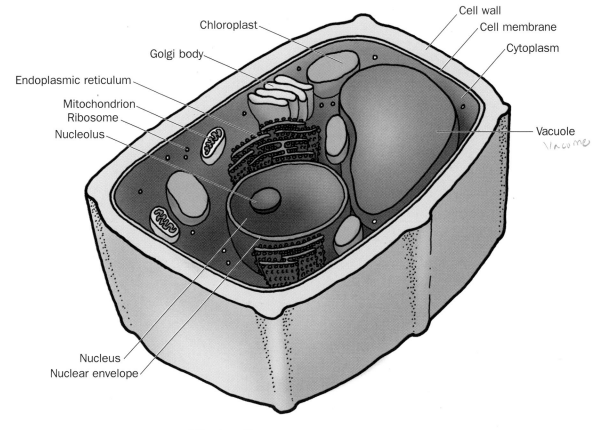

Plant cell

Getting Started

1. Work with your group to draw on a piece of newsprint what you think a typical cell looks like. Label any parts with which you are familiar.

2. Share your group's drawing with the class.

MATERIALS FOR LESSON 7

For you

1 copy of Student Sheet 7.1: Template for *Spirogyra* Cell Drawing

1 copy of Student Sheet 7.2: Template for Onion Leaf Cell Drawing

1 copy of Student Sheet 7.3: Template for *Elodea* Leaf Cell Drawings

1 copy of Student Sheet 7.4: Template for Animal Cell Drawings

1 box of colored pencils

For your group

1 set of organism photo cards

1 sheet of newsprint Several strands of *Spirogyra*

2 pieces of sliced onion

2 *Elodea* leaves soaked in fresh water

2 *Elodea* leaves soaked in salt solution

1 prepared slide of human cheek cells

1 prepared slide of mammalian nerve cells

2 compound light microscopes

2 plastic slides

2 coverslips

2 metric rulers, 30 cm (12 in.)

2 transparent rulers

1 dropper bottle of Lugol solution

1 plastic pipette

Inquiry 7.1
Observing, Drawing, and Measuring an Algal Cell

PROCEDURE

1. Read "Plant and Animal Cells: The Same, but Different," at the beginning of this lesson. Discuss the reading selection with the class and ask questions to clarify anything you do not understand.

2. Use a plastic pipette to obtain a small sample of water from the container marked "Spirogyra." Spirogyra is a type of common pond alga whose cells are joined in chains. Make sure that the sample includes from two to four of the green strands that are floating in the water.

3. Put a drop of the sample on the middle of the slide and add a coverslip.

4. Focus on a chain of Spirogyra cells under 100×. After observing Spirogyra through the microscope, discuss with your partner how you think it got its name.

5. Switch to 400× and focus on one cell (see Figure 7.1). Draw the cell in the circle on Student Sheet 7.1: Template for Spirogyra Drawing. Title your drawing, "Spirogyra Cell." Label at least two organelles. Refer to "Plant and Animal Cells: The Same, But Different" to help you identify the structures. Follow the guidelines for scientific drawings on Student Sheet 2.3A, which you used in Lesson 2.

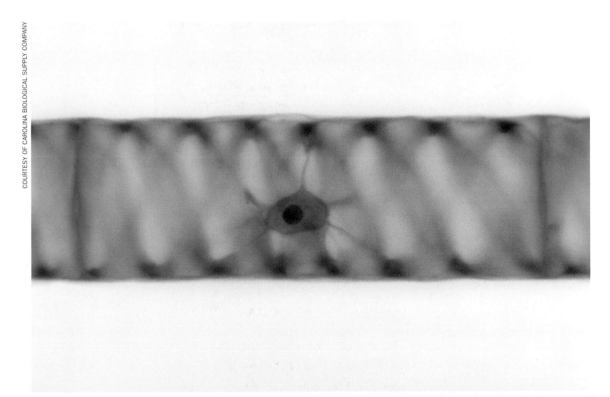

COURTESY OF CAROLINA BIOLOGICAL SUPPLY COMPANY

Figure 7.1 *With a good microscope and a little fine tuning, you can even see the nucleus in a* Spirogyra *cell.*

6. Using your transparent ruler as a cover-slip, measure the length of one *Spirogyra* cell, as seen in Figure 7.2. Record the measurement in parentheses to the right of the title below the circle.

7. Review your drawing to ensure that you have followed each guideline. Follow your teacher's directions for turning in your drawing.

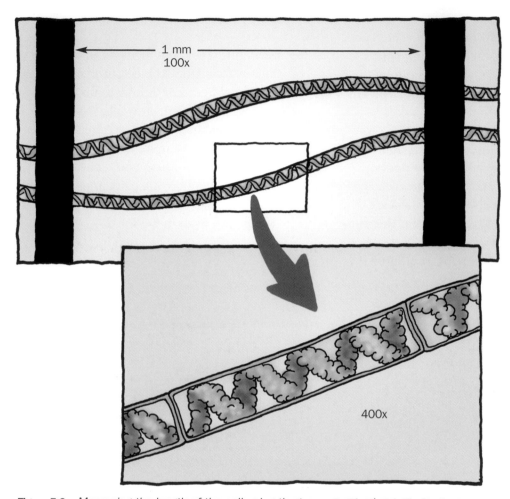

Figure 7.2 *Measuring the length of the cell using the transparent ruler*

Inquiry 7.2
Observing, Drawing, and Measuring an Onion Leaf Cell

PROCEDURE

1. Follow these steps to prepare a wet-mount slide of a leaf cell from the bulb of an onion plant:

A. Obtain a piece of sliced onion from the container provided by your teacher.

B. Follow the steps in Figure 7.3 to prepare a wet-mount slide of an onion leaf.

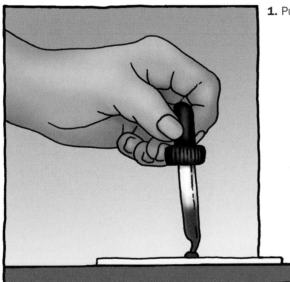

1. Put one drop of Lugol solution in the middle of a plastic slide.

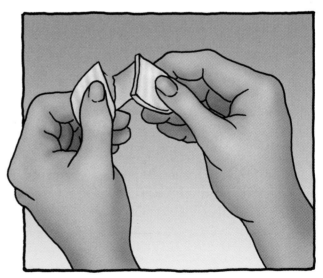

2. Bend the piece of onion against the curve until it snaps. Push one side under the other to peel off a thin membrane of leaf epidermis.

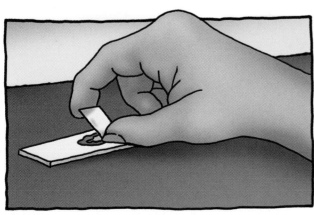

3. Spread the membrane out in the Lugol solution so that it is flat on the slide. Add a coverslip.

Figure 7.3 *How to prepare onion leaf membrane for viewing under the microscope*

2. Take turns with your partner to prepare a drawing of one onion leaf cell under high magnification. Draw the cell in the circle on Student Sheet 7.2: Template for Onion Leaf Cell Drawing. Follow the guidelines for scientific drawings. Title your drawing "Onion Leaf Cell." Label the cell wall, nucleus, and cytoplasm. Discuss with your partner why you cannot see chloroplasts in these cells even though these are plant cells.

3. Use the transparent ruler to measure the length of the cell. Record the measurement in the appropriate place on your drawing.

4. When you and your partner have completed your drawings, rinse and dry your slide, coverslip, and transparent ruler, and proceed to the next inquiry.

Inquiry 7.3
Observing, Drawing, and Measuring *Elodea* Leaf Cells

PROCEDURE

1. Follow your teacher's directions to obtain one *Elodea* leaf that is soaking in fresh water. *Elodea* is a common, freshwater plant whose leaves are good specimens for observing typical plant leaf cells.

2. Place the leaf on the slide and add a coverslip. Focus on a layer of cells under 100×. Switch to 400× and focus on a smaller group of cells. With your partner, discuss which structure you can see in these cells that were not present in the onion leaf cells.

3. Draw one cell in the upper circle on Student Sheet 7.3: Template for *Elodea* Leaf Cell Drawings. Title your drawing "*Elodea* Leaf Cell." Label three of its organelles. Use the transparent ruler to measure the length of one cell. Record the length in the appropriate place on your drawing.

4. Clean your slide and then obtain a second *Elodea* leaf that has been soaking in salt water. Set up your slide as you did for the *Elodea* that had been soaking in fresh water. Move the slide around to find a cell whose contents have shrunk into a round or oval shape. Draw one cell under 400× in the lower circle on Student Sheet 7.3. Label the same three organelles as you did in Procedure Step 3. Also label a fourth organelle that has become visible because water has been forced out of the cell by the salt solution.

5. Rinse and dry your slide, coverslip, and transparent ruler.

Inquiry 7.4
Exploring Animal Cells

PROCEDURE

1. Have one member of your group obtain one prepared slide of mammalian epithelial tissue (cheek cells) and one of mammalian nerve tissue.

2. Take turns with your partner to observe, draw, and measure one cell from one of the prepared slides. When each pair in your group is finished with its drawing, trade slides. Draw one slide in each of the circles on Student Sheet 7.4: Template for Animal Cell Drawings.

3. Title the appropriate drawing "Cheek Cell." Label the cell membrane, cytoplasm, and nucleus.

4. Title the other drawing "Nerve Cell." Label the cell membrane, cytoplasm, and nucleus. Refer to Figure 7.4 if you have difficulty identifying a cell within the nerve tissue.

5. Look at the cells in your drawings and those in Figures 7.5 and 7.6. Discuss with your partner why these cells are so different in size and shape.

6. Work with others in your group to update your organism photo cards for *Spirogyra, Elodea,* and humans. Return them to your teacher.

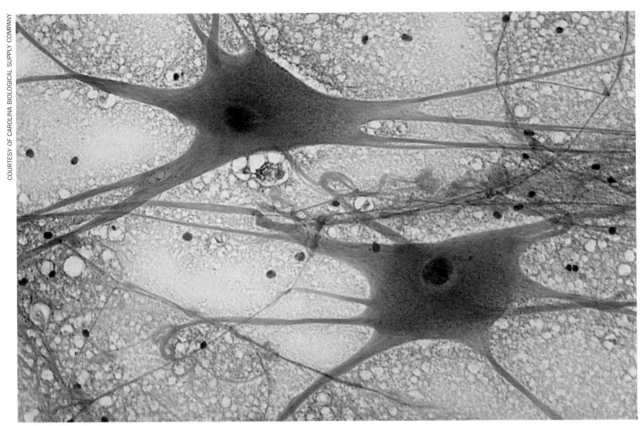

COURTESY OF CAROLINA BIOLOGICAL SUPPLY COMPANY

Figure 7.4 *Animal cells are often difficult to distinguish on a slide. This photo should help you with your identification. The cell membrane, cytoplasm, and nucleus in these two nerve cells are clearly visible.*

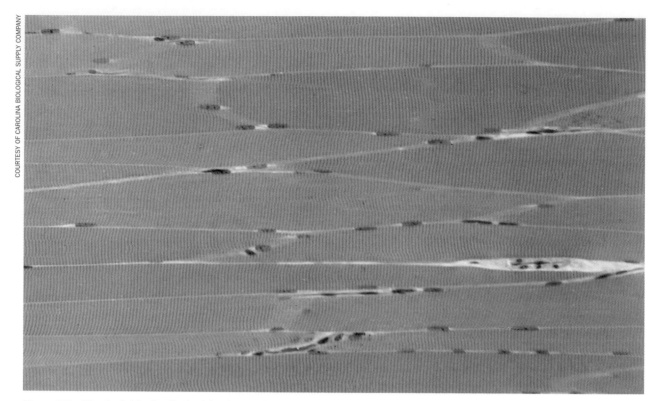

Figure 7.5 *The individual cells in this photo of skeletal muscle—taken through a microscope at approximately 400x—are long, narrow, and so tightly packed that they are difficult to identify.*

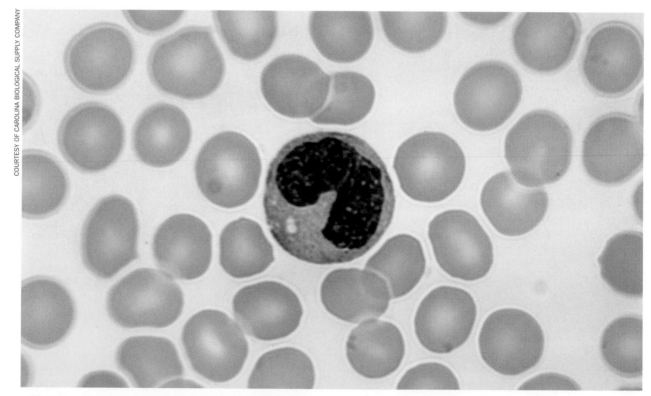

Figure 7.6 *This photo of highly magnified blood tissue contains many red blood cells and one white blood cell, right in the center.*

REFLECTING ON WHAT YOU'VE DONE

Answer the following questions on the student sheets indicated.

A. Based on the algal *Spirogyra* that you observed, would you consider *Spirogyra* to be more plant-like or animal-like? Defend your answer. (Student Sheet 7.1)

B. Why do you think the bulb of the onion plant is so big? What function does it serve for the plant? (Student Sheet 7.2)

C. What happened to the *Elodea* leaf cells when they were soaked in salt solution? How do you think this relates to what happens when you eat salty foods? (Student Sheet 7.3)

D. Use the Venn diagram to show the cell structures and organelles that you observed in cells from the onion bulb, *Elodea* leaf, and epithelial tissue. (Student Sheet 7.4)

E. If animal cells do not have cell walls, what gives animals such as mammals shape and support? (Student Sheet 7.4)

F. Give one example from among the cells you observed in this lesson of how the size and shape of a cell is well suited for its particular function. (Student Sheet 7.4)

G. Compare the cells you drew in the inquiries with the one your group sketched during "Getting Started." Based on what you have learned, discuss with the class what you should do to make your sketch more accurate. (Student Sheet 7.4)

Cell Division: Multiplying by Dividing

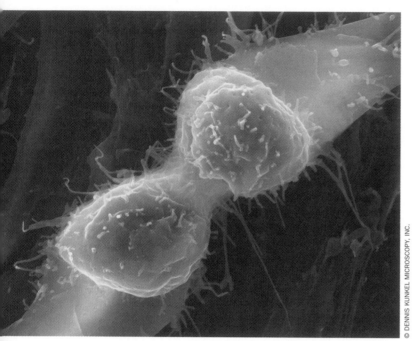

© DENNIS KUNKEL MICROSCOPY, INC.

When you look through a microscope like the one you're using in class, cells often appear two-dimensional. But this photo of a dividing cell shows the true three-dimensional quality of cells. It was taken through a powerful electron microscope.

INTRODUCTION

In Lesson 7, you looked at several different types of cells and observed some of their major structures and organelles. In Lesson 9, you will explore sexual reproduction in flowering plants. To bridge the gap between these two lessons, you will now learn how cells reproduce.

The title of this lesson seems contradictory, but in the world of cells it's not. Cell division is one of the most important processes in living things. Its only purpose is multiplication! In this lesson, you will use pipe cleaners to depict what takes place just before and during cell division. Then you will create models to represent specific stages of this process.

OBJECTIVES FOR THIS LESSON

Depict the behavior of chromosomes during interphase and cell division.

Construct models that depict interphase and the key steps of cell division.

Compare and contrast cell division in plant and animal cells.

Update organism photo cards for those organisms whose cells undergo cell division.

Getting Started

1. With your teacher and classmates, read "Multiply, Divide, and Survive."

2. Discuss the reading selection with the class and ask your teacher to clarify any aspect of mitosis and cell division that you don't understand.

Inquiry 8.1
Simulating Interphase, Mitosis, and Cytokinesis

PROCEDURE

1. Work with your partner to cut three pipe cleaners. Follow these steps:

A. Place one end of a pipe cleaner against the zero line of the metric ruler.

B. Place a mark on the pipe cleaner at 4-cm intervals. Repeat this with the two other pipe cleaners.

C. Use your scissors to cut the pipe cleaners at the marks you made. You will use four of these pieces of pipe cleaner for this inquiry. Set the rest aside for Inquiry 8.2.

MATERIALS FOR LESSON 8

For your group

1 set of organism photo cards
2 copies of Student Sheet 8.2: Interphase and Stages of Mitosis
6 pipe cleaners
2 pairs of scissors
2 metric rulers, 30 cm (12 in.)
2 small resealable plastic bags
2 black markers
Transparent tape

2. Watch and listen as your teacher uses a set of transparencies and pipe cleaners to demonstrate the behavior of chromosomes during interphase and mitosis.

3. Now, follow your teacher's example for using your four pipe cleaner pieces to depict the action of chromosomes during interphase and mitosis.

Inquiry 8.2
Creating a Model of Interphase and the Stages of Mitosis

PROCEDURE

1. Work in pairs to create "snapshots" of a pair of duplicated chromosomes during interphase and mitosis. You will use 4-cm pieces of pipe cleaner to represent the single and duplicated chromosomes. To make all the models, you and your partner will need a total of 16 4-cm pieces.

2. On the basis of what you now know about cell division, arrange in order the pages of Student Sheet 8.2: Interphase and Stages of Mitosis. Decide with your group which pages will have no pipe cleaners.

3. Make a model of a duplicated chromosome by twisting two pipe cleaners around each other once near the middle to form a narrow X, as shown in Figure 8.1.

4. Use the remaining pipe cleaners to illustrate how the chromosomes appear in each of the remaining phases.

5. Lay out the pipe cleaners in the appropriate arrangements on the pages of your student sheet. The outlines of the cells and fibers have been drawn to help you place your pipe cleaners. As references, use the reading selection "Multiply, Divide, and Survive" and Figures 8.2 and 8.3, which show cells in the process of dividing. Ask your teacher for approval before you tape the pipe cleaners to the sheet.

6. When your teacher has approved your layout, attach each pipe cleaner to the student sheet with transparent tape.

Figure 8.1 *You now have a model of a duplicated chromosome. Notice the narrow area where the duplicated chromosomes are joined. This is called the centromere.*

7. Follow your teacher's directions for cleaning up and turning in your work.

8. Update your organism photo cards for any organism you have studied whose cells undergo mitosis.

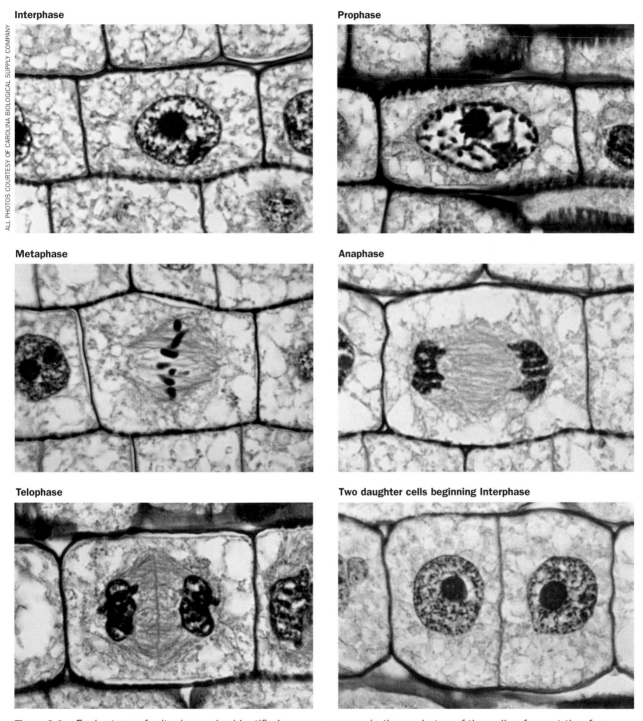

Figure 8.2 *Each stage of mitosis can be identified, as you can see in these photos of the cells of a root tip of an onion plant under high magnification.*

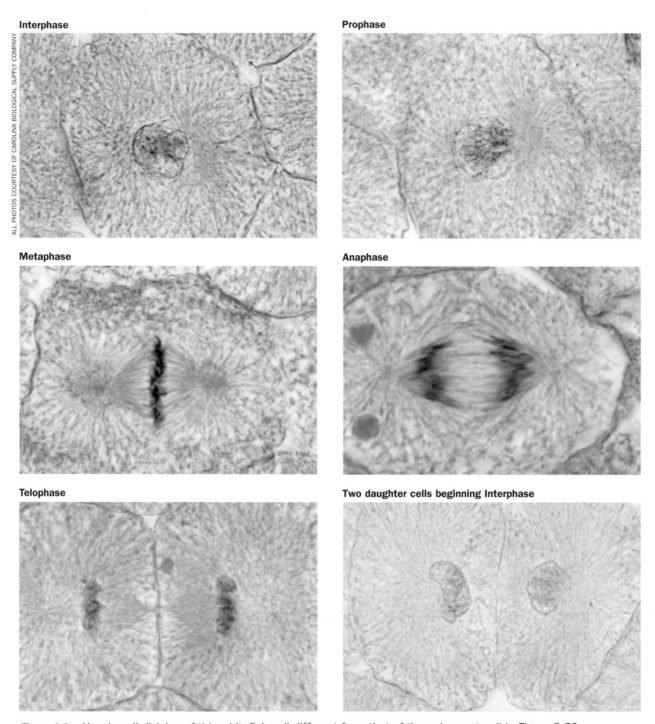

ALL PHOTOS COURTESY OF CAROLINA BIOLOGICAL SUPPLY COMPANY

Interphase

Prophase

Metaphase

Anaphase

Telophase

Two daughter cells beginning Interphase

Figure 8.3 *How is cell division of this whitefish cell different from that of the onion root cell in Figure 8.2?*

REFLECTING ON WHAT YOU'VE DONE

1. Respond in your science notebook to the following:

   A. Your classmates David and Linda are discussing cell division. David says that this process is important in order for organisms to grow. Linda says that it is important so that organisms can reproduce. Who is right and who is wrong? Why?

   B. Explain why cell division is a rather misleading name for the process.

   C. How is cytokinesis different in plant and animal cells?

2. Visit the STC/MS™ Web site (http://www.stcms.si.edu) and follow the appropriate links for more information about mitosis. Be sure to check out the animations of mitosis.

Multiply, Divide, and Survive

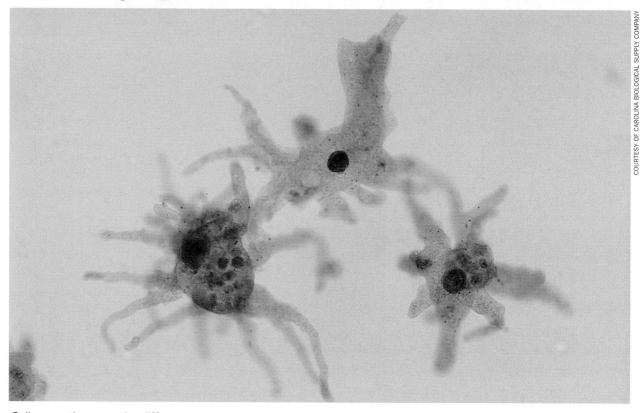

COURTESY OF CAROLINA BIOLOGICAL SUPPLY COMPANY

Cells sometimes require different stains to highlight various organelles. This often results in a colorful slide.

Late in the 19th century, scientists developed dyes to stain cell structures so they could be seen more clearly through a microscope. This technique, called "staining," allowed scientists for the first time to observe cells in different stages of their life cycles. They could see what happens as cells grow and divide.

As a result of these studies, scientists now know that most cells containing nuclei undergo a series of steps, called "mitosis" and "cytokinesis," to divide into two cells. The stages of mitosis and cytokinesis are collectively called "cell division."

Using their newly developed dyes, those 19th-century scientists also were able to observe some rod-shaped structures in the nuclei that became noticeable just before the cells began to split. Those structures are called "chromosomes." Chromosomes, composed of a sub-stance called "DNA" (deoxyribonucleic acid), are very important because they contain all of the hereditary information for each organism.

Pairing Up

Chromosomes occur in pairs. Although the number of chromosome pairs varies among organisms, all members of the same species have a unique number.

You might expect that complex organisms would have a greater number of chromosomes than simpler organisms. This is not the case. For example, humans have 23 pairs of chromosomes in each body cell, while rose plants, which are less complex, have 35 pairs. Wisconsin Fast Plants have 10 pairs of chromosomes. Fruit flies have 4 pairs. Hereditary units called "genes" appear in the same locations on both chromosomes of each pair.

Structure of a chromosome

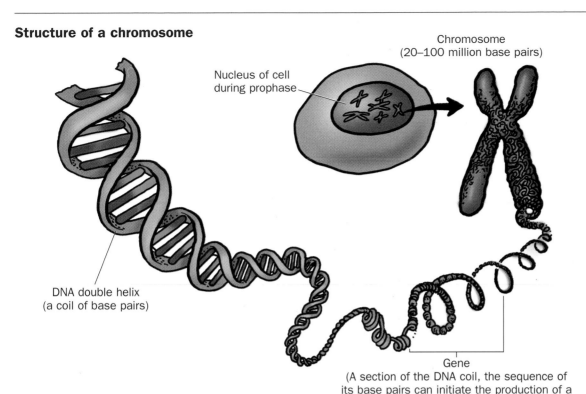

Nucleus of cell
during prophase

Chromosome
(20–100 million base pairs)

DNA double helix
(a coil of base pairs)

Gene
(A section of the DNA coil, the sequence of
its base pairs can initiate the production of a
protein that determines a genetic trait.)

Going in Circles

Like humans, cells have a life cycle. The cell's life cycle has stages, or phases. When cells are not dividing, they are in a stage called "interphase." During this phase, cells are busy carrying on their life processes, which include growing. The chromosomes are not visible because they are elongated and blend into the rest of the nuclear material. In this condition, they are referred to as "chromatin." The DNA, which makes up the threads of chromatin, duplicates during this phase. Near the end of interphase, the cell makes its final preparations for mitosis by producing the necessary organelles for each daughter cell. Because the chromatin threads are still elongated at this point, they are not yet recognizable, even under a compound microscope. A cell in this stage might look like the one shown here.

(continued)

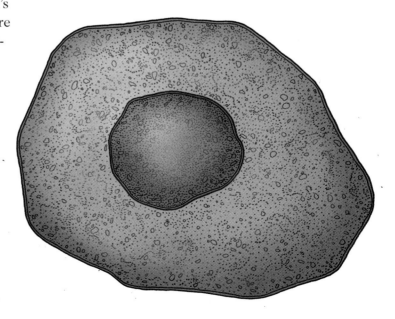

By the end of interphase, the chromosomes have duplicated. At this point human cells have 46 doubled chromosomes in their nuclei.

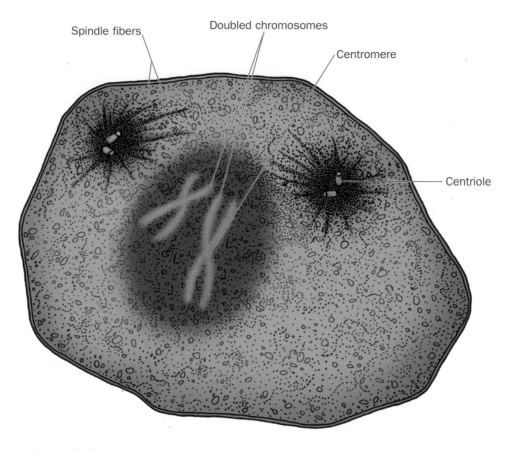

Spindle fibers

Doubled chromosomes

Centromere

Centriole

This is how an animal cell might look toward the end of prophase. Only two of the doubled chromosomes are shown.

Mitosis consists of a series of phases during which the DNA, which duplicates during interphase, first coils and condenses into chromosomes. Then the chromosomes detach from each other and separate into the nuclei of what will soon become two new cells. These new cells are known as "daughter cells." Although scientists describe the process of mitosis as having four phases—prophase, metaphase, anaphase, and telophase—it is actually continuous. Each phase passes smoothly into the next. Dividing mitosis into phases is comparable to viewing a movie, then selecting individual frames, or "snapshots," that best represent each part of the movie.

During prophase, the chromatin threads begin to coil. They shorten and become much thicker. At this point they are referred to as chromosomes and can be observed through a compound microscope. A mesh-like structure of fine, spindle fibers develops. As the nuclear envelope disintegrates, these fibers guide the movements of the chromosomes. As though they were being tugged along by the fibers, the duplicated chromosomes begin to move toward the middle of the cell.

During metaphase, the chromosomes line up in the middle of the cell. Their centromeres, which are the places where the duplicated chromosomes are attached, align in the exact middle of the cell.

At the beginning of anaphase, the duplicated chromosomes separate. Each becomes an individual chromosome. The fibers shorten, drawing the chromosomes to opposite ends of the cell.

As soon as the chromosomes reach the ends of the cell, telophase begins. This phase is almost the opposite of prophase. The chromosomes uncoil and elongate and begin to blend into the nuclear material. A nuclear envelope forms around each new nucleus. The fibers break down and disappear. Mitosis is now complete. The daughter cells are considered to be in interphase. The two nuclei that result are identical. This means that their DNA, or genetic material, is identical.

Now, the final step in the process, cytokinesis, must occur. During this process, the daughter cells split from each other. There is a major difference between cytokinesis in plant and in animal cells. In an animal cell, the cell membrane pinches inward and forms two separate daughter cells. In a plant cell, a cell plate begins forming in the middle of the cell and grows outward until it becomes a part of the cell wall between the daughter cells. Cell walls help give the plant support. Animal cells have no cell walls.

The illustration below summarizes the stages in the cell cycle. ❑

The cell cycle

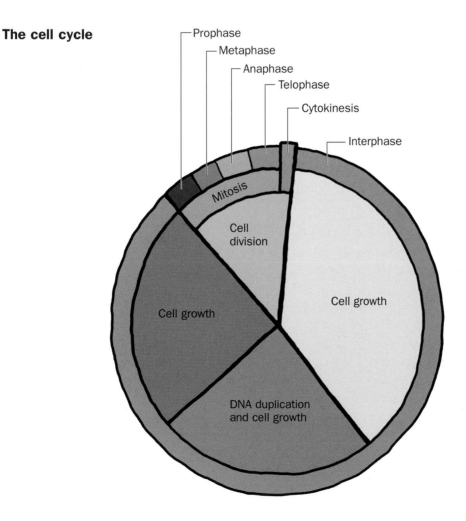

Sexual Reproduction in Flowering Plants

CORBIS/ROYALTY-FREE

While this hummingbird feeds on nectar from the flower, it may also provide a valuable service for the plant. Can you guess what that service is?

INTRODUCTION

What are flowers for? Many of them are beautiful, but what function do they serve for plants? In this lesson, you will discover answers to these questions. You will examine a flower to observe its structures. Then you will apply what you learned when you work with your Wisconsin Fast Plants flowers. You'll be busy as a bee in this lesson—in more ways than one!

OBJECTIVES FOR THIS LESSON

Examine two or more flowers and develop an understanding of their structures and functions.

Cross-pollinate the Wisconsin Fast Plants flowers in your growing system.

Explain several ways in which flowers are pollinated in nature.

Demonstrate an understanding of the difference between cell division and meiosis.

Update the Wisconsin Fast Plants organism photo card.

Getting Started

1. Follow along as student volunteers read "Methods of Reproduction." Ask questions to clarify points you do not understand.

2. The Fast Plants in your growing system should be flowering by now. Briefly observe a Fast Plants flower and the flower you brought to class. With your group, discuss and agree on the function of a flower. Describe that function in one sentence on a fresh page in your science notebook.

3. Share your ideas with the class and participate as your teacher guides your class in a discussion about flowering plants.

MATERIALS FOR
LESSON 9

For you

1 copy of Student Sheet 9.1: Template for Flower Drawings

For your group

1 set of organism photo cards
2 perfect flowers
2 hand lenses
2 compound light microscopes
2 plastic slides
2 coverslips
2 cotton swabs
2 scalpels
1 black marker

Figure 9.1 *These students are comparing a Fast Plants flower with the one they brought to class, seeking to determine a flower's function.*

Inquiry 9.1
Dissecting a Perfect Flower

PROCEDURE

1. With the class, discuss Figure 9.2.

2. You will work with your partner for this inquiry; however, you will each do your own drawing. Observe carefully the flower you brought to class. Place it in a position that allows you to see it clearly. You may need to bend the front petals down for a better view. Sketch your flower in the upper circle on Student Sheet 9.1: Template for Flower Drawings. Title your drawing "XXX—A Perfect Flower." Replace "XXX" with the name of your flower. For example, if you drew a tulip, your title would be "Tulip— A Perfect Flower." Use Figure 9.2 to help you identify each flower part and observe the characteristics of a perfect flower.

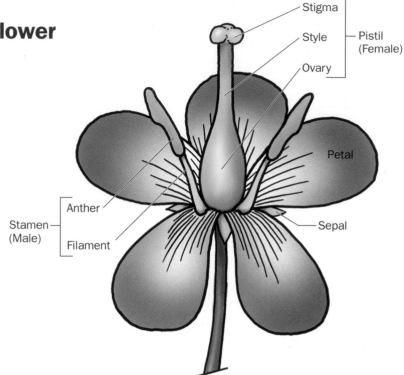

Figure 9.2 *A perfect flower contains both male and female reproductive structures. What do you think an imperfect flower is?*

3. Use your scalpel to cut and remove an entire stamen, one of the male reproductive structures, from your flower. Draw the stamen in the lower circle on the front of Student Sheet 9.1. Label the anther and filament. Title your drawing "Male Reproductive Structure—The Stamen."

SAFETY TIP

Always cut in a direction away from your fingers when using a scalpel.

Inquiry 9.2
Pollinating the Fa[...]
Flowers

PROCEDURE

1. Locate the pistil of one [...] Plants flowers. Use Figu[...]

2. Collect pollen with a co[...] ton swab by dabbing the[...] swab gently onto the anthers of a Fast Plants[...] flower. Next, dab the sw[...] onto the stigma of one o[...] more Fast Plants flowers[...] on another plant, as sho[...] in Figure 9.7. The proce[...] of transferring pollen fro[...] a flower of one plant to [...] flower of another plant i[...] called cross-pollination. Repeat the process unti[...] you have cross-pollinate[...] each of the flowers in yo[...] growing system.

4. Tap the anther of your flower against the top surface of a microscope slide. Pollen is likely to fall from the anther onto the slide. If it does not, use the tip of your pencil to scrape pollen from the anther and put it on the slide.

5. Add a coverslip. Center a pollen grain in the field of view and bring it into focus under a magnification of 100×; then switch to a magnification of 400× and refocus.

6. Divide the upper circle on the back of Student Sheet 9.1 into three equal sections. Mark the three sections "A," "B," and "C." Print the title "Pollen Grains" below the circle. Draw a pollen grain from your flower in section A. Label the pollen grain with the name of the flower. Then trade slides with a pair of students that has pollen grains from a flower of a different species. Follow Step 5 again to get a pollen grain in focus under 400×. Draw the grain in Section B of the upper circle. Label this pollen grain with the appropriate name. Compare these pollen grains with the highly magnified grains of a ragweed plant shown in Figure 9.3.

7. Clean your slide. Remove a stamen from one of your Fast Plants flowers and scrape some of its pollen onto the slide. View the Fast Plants pollen under a magnification of 400×. Draw one of the pollen grains in Section C of the upper circle. Label this pollen grain "Fast Plants Pollen Grain." Discuss with your partner why the pollen grains of different species appear so dissimilar. Also discuss how pollen moves from one plant to another.

Figure 9.3 *This is a photo of ragweed pollen taken through an electron microscope. You may be allergic to this pollen.*

COURTESY OF CAROLINA BIOLOGICAL SUPPLY COMPANY

Figure 9.7 *Make sure you transfer[...]*

8. Remove the pe
and the remain
stamens from y
flower and set
aside. The only
flower part left
be the pistil, th
female reprodu
structure. Use y
scalpel to cut th
pistil across the
middle of the
ovary, as shown
Figure 9.4. Note
safety procedur
followed by the
dent in Figure 9
Use your hand
if necessary to
observe the
columns of imn
ovules, in the c

9. Clean your slide
the tip of your s
slide. Use your
the ovule under

REFLECTING ON WHAT YOU'VE DONE
On the basis of what you have learned about
reproduction in flowering plants, answer the following questions on Student Sheet 9.1:

A. Using "The Wonder of Flowering
Plants" as a reference, explain what happens inside the flower after pollination.

B. What do you think will develop as the
flowers wither? Hint: Think about the
name of the structure that protects the
seeds.

C. Why do you think some flowers have
so many pollen grains and ovules?

COURTESY OF HENRY MILNE/© NSRC

Figure 9.
scalpel

METHODS OF REPRODUCTION

Asexual Reproduction

In Lesson 8, you learned about the cell cycle. Cell division, an important part of that cycle, enables multicellular organisms, such as humans, to grow by producing more cells. For single-celled organisms, cell division is often the only method of reproduction. Cell division does not involve the union of male and female sex cells. When new organisms are formed from a single parent, without the union of male and female sex cells, the process is known as "asexual reproduction." Asexual means "without sex."

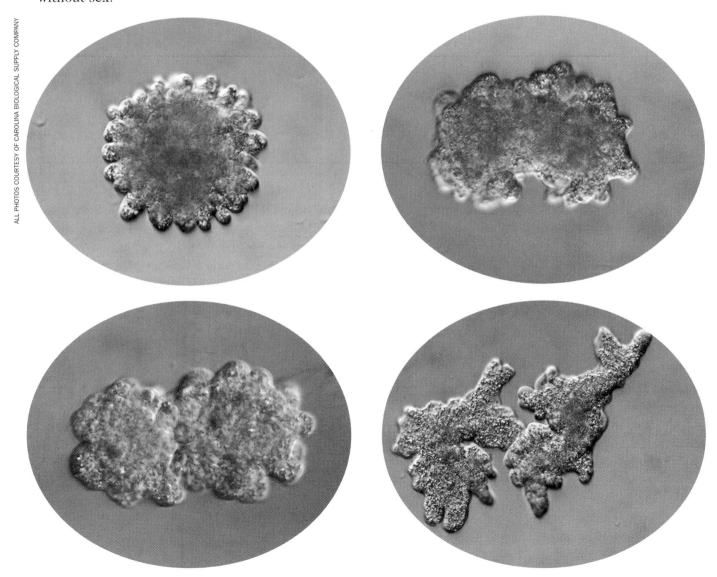

ALL PHOTOS COURTESY OF CAROLINA BIOLOGICAL SUPPLY COMPANY

This is an amoeba reproducing by fission, a form of cell division and asexual reproduction.

The Wonder of Flowering Plants

It takes both male and female sex cells to create a human being, through a process called "sexual reproduction." The same is true for many flowering plants. The flower is the reproductive organ of a flowering plant.

Within the flower are male structures called "stamens" and one or more female structures called "pistils." The stamen consists of the anther, which produces the pollen, and the filament, which supports the anther. The pollen contains the sperm nuclei. At the top of the pistil is the sticky stigma, which is supported by a structure called a style. At the bottom of the style is the ovary, which produces the eggs (ovules). Each egg contains an egg nucleus.

Some species of plants have flowers that include both male and female structures—that is, both stamen and pistil. Others have only the male or female structure. A flower that has both a male and female reproductive structure is called a "perfect flower." A flower that has only male or female reproductive structures is referred to as an "imperfect flower." (These names are historical ones. Perhaps if we named them now, we'd use the terms "complete" and "incomplete.") The illustration shows a perfect flower on the top and two imperfect flowers on the bottom.

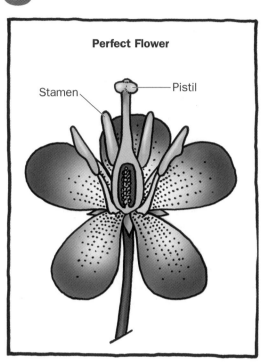

Perfect Flower

Stamen — Pistil

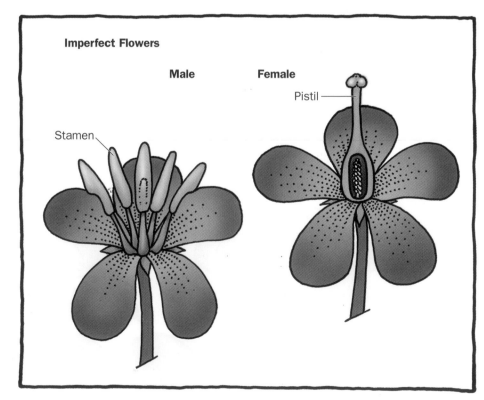

Imperfect Flowers

Male   **Female**

Pistil

Stamen

For a plant to make seeds, pollen from an anther must contact the sticky stigma of a pistil. This is called "pollination." There are two kinds of pollination—self-pollination and cross-pollination. Self-pollination occurs when pollen is transferred to the stigma of a flower on the same plant. Cross-pollination occurs when pollen is transferred to the stigma of a flower on another plant of the same species. Some species of plants, such as Fast Plants, cannot self-pollinate. In order for seeds to be produced in Fast Plants, cross-pollination must occur. In general, plants that cross-pollinate need pollen from their own species.

Self-pollination is pretty simple. Gravity, an insect, a gust of wind, or even a raindrop can accomplish the task easily. Cross-pollination, by contrast, requires pollen to move from one plant to another. Without the help of wind, water, and animals like insects, pollination would not occur as often and many flowers would fail to make seeds. Without seeds, there would be fewer new plants.

Notice the many pollen grains sticking to the hairs on the bee's body.

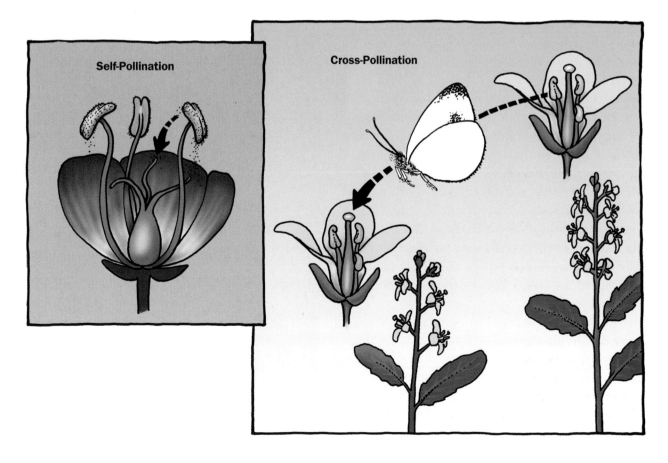

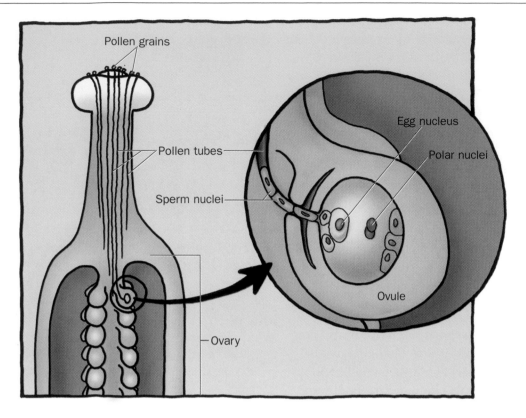

Pollen grains

Pollen tubes

Sperm nuclei

Ovary

Egg nucleus

Polar nuclei

Ovule

Pollen grains generally contain three nuclei—two sperm nuclei and one tube nucleus. When the pollen lands on the stigma of a flower of the same species, the tube nucleus begins forming a tube that grows down to the ovary. The two sperm nuclei then move down the tube to the ovary. The waiting ovule contains an egg nucleus, two polar nuclei that fuse, and five other nuclei that eventually disintegrate. One sperm nucleus unites with the egg nucleus in an ovule. This process is called "fertilization." After fertilization occurs, the egg begins to develop into a seed.

The other sperm nucleus unites with the fused polar nuclei in the center of the egg. This stimulates the formation of a substance called endosperm, which is food for the developing embryo. One or more seed coats develop around the growing embryo.

At this point, the flower withers, and the ovary develops into a structure called a fruit. Some fruits, such as cherries and oranges, are edible by humans, and some, such as the dry pods of the Fast Plants, are inedible. The fruit helps protect the seeds and serves as a way to disperse them. Some fruits, like cherries, contain only one seed; others, like oranges and squash, contain many seeds. A squash, cut lengthwise, has the familiar shape of most flower ovaries.

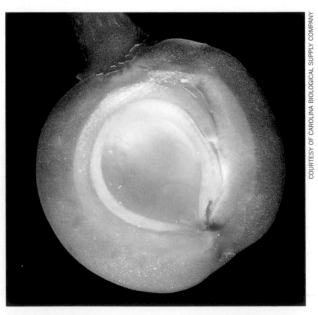

There was only one seed in this dissected cherry.

Notice the orderly arrangement of seeds in this orange slice.

The squash, cut lengthwise, retains the original shape of the ovary. It's larger now because of the stored food.

While flowers are necessary for sexual reproduction in many plants, they also provide us with a source of natural beauty.

Because a flower's real function is to promote pollination, fertilization, and seed production, it is not surprising that flowers have developed many ways to make these processes more efficient. Since plants are rooted and cannot move about, flowers have adapted in ways that encourage visits by potential pollinators, such as bees or hummingbirds. In some ways, flowers are like people. When people want to attract attention, they may wear cologne and put on bright, colorful clothes. Some flowers, too, have strong scents and a rainbow of colors that attract attention from bees, butterflies, and other animals. ☐

10
Leaf Structure and Transpiration

© JOEL SARTORE/CORBIS

Leaves provide food and shade as well as fun, but what function do they serve for the plant?

INTRODUCTION

Have you wondered what happens to all that water that disappears from the reservoir of your growing system? Although some might have evaporated from the soil, you are probably aware that much of it is absorbed by the roots of your Fast Plants. But where does it go from there? Is it all used by the plant? Does any water escape from your plants? If so, how? Let's find out.

OBJECTIVES FOR THIS LESSON

Determine the change in volume of nutrient solution in the reservoir of your growing system over 24 hours.

Determine whether there is a relationship between the volume of nutrient solution that passes through your Fast Plants growing system in 24 hours and the number of leaves on the plants.

Observe and draw a stomatal unit from the epidermis of a lettuce leaf.

Use a model to demonstrate how guard cells operate to form a stoma.

Explain how the structure of a dicot leaf helps control the water flow in a plant.

Learn about photosynthesis, the process during which green plants produce glucose and release oxygen into the air.

Update your organism photo cards for *Lemna* and Wisconsin Fast Plants.

Getting Started

1. Remove the planter from the reservoir of your growing system. Empty the nutrient solution from the reservoir into the graduated cylinder until it reaches the 250-mL mark. Discard any solution remaining in the reservoir.

2. If you have less than 250 mL of nutrient solution in the graduated cylinder, add more until it contains exactly 250 mL. Pour the 250 mL of nutrient solution into the reservoir and replace the planter. Record the volume of nutrient solution that is now in the reservoir in the space provided on Student Sheet 10.3.

3. With your group, count the total number of leaves on the Fast Plants in your growing system. Record this number in the space provided on Student Sheet 10.3.

MATERIALS FOR LESSON 10

For you
- 1 copy of Student Sheet 10.1: Template for Stomatal Unit Drawing
- 1 copy of Student Sheet 10.2: Stomatal Unit Model
- 1 copy of Student Sheet 10.3: Transpiration in Wisconsin Fast Plants

For your group
- 1 Fast Plants growing system
- 1 set of organism photo cards
- 2 plastic slides
- 2 coverslips
- 2 compound light microscopes
- 2 plastic pipettes
- 1 piece of string, 12 cm
- Tap water
- 1 plastic cup, 16 oz
- 1 piece of dialysis membrane, 30 cm
- 2 pieces of lettuce leaf
- 2 *Lemna* plants
- 1 250-mL graduated cylinder
- 2 scalpels
- 2 dissecting needles

Inquiry 10.1
Observing and Drawing a Stomatal Unit From the Epidermis of a Lettuce Leaf

PROCEDURE

1. Follow the steps in Figure 10.1 (see next page) to prepare a lettuce leaf membrane to view under the microscope.

2. Focus on the epidermis with your microscope under low power (100×). Locate a stomatal unit, which will look like a small, bright "eye" among the larger epidermal cells of the membrane. Center a stoma in the field of view then switch to high power (400×). Draw and label the stoma, guard cells, and nuclei in the circle on Student Sheet 10.1, using Figure 10.2 and "Looking at Leaves" at the end of this lesson as a reference. Title your drawing "Stomatal Unit."

3. Discard the lettuce membrane and rinse your slide and coverslip. Obtain a *Lemna* plant from the culture container.

4. Place the plant on the slide with the roots facing down. Add a coverslip. Focus on the upper epidermis of the leaf under low power; then switch to high power. Move the slide to locate the stomata.

Most dicot leaves, including those of Fast Plants, have the majority of their stomata on the lower epidermis. Discuss with your group why a *Lemna* leaf has most of its stomata on its upper epidermis.

5. Complete the "Reflecting on What You've Done" questions on Student Sheet 10.1.

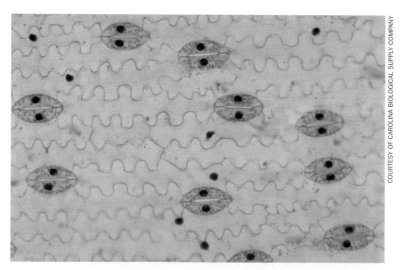

COURTESY OF CAROLINA BIOLOGICAL SUPPLY COMPANY

Figure 10.2 *Each stomatal unit is composed of two bean-shaped guard cells and the stoma, or opening, between them, as seen in this epidermis of a lily leaf magnified 400 times.*

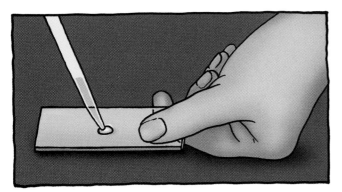

1. Use a plastic pipette to place a drop of water in the center of a plastic slide.

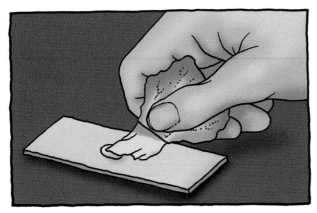

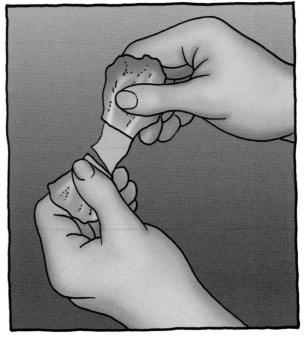

2. Take a small piece of a lettuce leaf and bend it against the curve until it snaps. Then slowly move one side under the other so that a clear, thin portion, or membrane, of the epidermis is peeled off and hanging from one of the sides.

3. Ease the thin portion of epidermis onto the drop of water on the plastic slide while it is still connected to the piece of lettuce. Use your scalpel to detach the membrane from the larger piece. If you have difficulty doing this, ask your teacher for help.

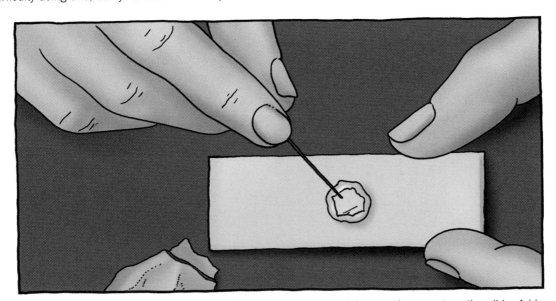

4. Use the tip of your dissecting needle, if necessary, to spread the membrane out on the slide. Add a coverslip.

Figure 10.1 *Preparing a slide of a membrane of a lettuce leaf*

Inquiry 10.2
Preparing a Model of a Stomatal Unit

PROCEDURE

1. Put about 5 cm of tap water into your 16-oz plastic cup. Obtain a membrane from the container, submerge it in the water in the cup, and take it back to your desk.

2. Remove the membrane from the water. Fold it in half so that the two ends meet. Rub one end of the membrane between your thumb and index finger until it opens into a tubular shape, as shown in Figure 10.3. Remoisten it as necessary to keep it open. Repeat this to open the other end of the membrane.

3. Ensure that both halves of the membrane are open at the top. Take it to your teacher. Hold both ends of the membrane open and facing upward while your teacher adds a green sugar solution to the membrane until it is about two-thirds full, as shown in Figure 10.4.

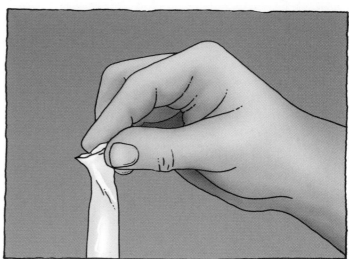

Figure 10.3 *While the end of the membrane is still moist, rub it between your thumb and forefinger until it opens into a tubular shape.*

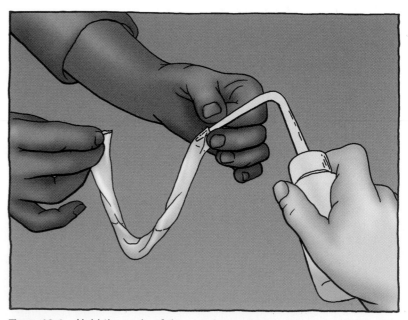

Figure 10.4 *Hold the ends of the membrane firmly while your teacher fills it two-thirds full with sugar solution. Can you guess why the solution has been dyed green?*

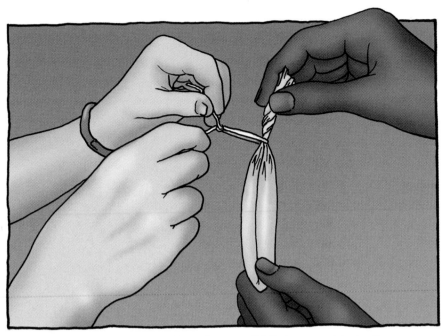

Figure 10.5 *Make sure you tie the string very tightly to prevent leakage.*

4. Twist the open ends of the membrane together to take up the slack. Then tie them together with string at the point where the twist stops and the liquid starts, as shown in Figure 10.5. Rinse the outside of the membrane and the plastic cup thoroughly with tap water.

5. Lay the membrane in the plastic cup. Position the membrane so that the two sides are flush against each other. Add fresh tap water to the cup to a depth of about 2 cm. After being positioned in the cup, your membrane should appear as in Figure 10.6.

6. Let the membrane sit in the water until your teacher directs you to observe it again. Then draw your observations on Student Sheet 10.2, and answer the questions under "Reflecting on What You've Done" on the Student Sheet.

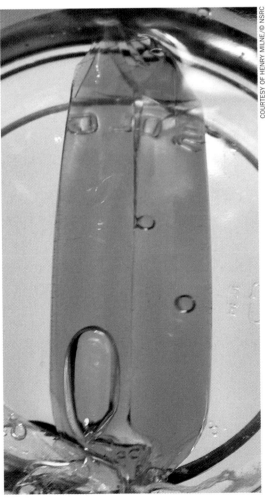

COURTESY OF HENRY MILNE/© NSRC

Figure 10.6 *The two membranes should be flush against each other, with no space between them.*

Inquiry 10.3
Exploring Transpiration in Wisconsin Fast Plants

PROCEDURE

1. Use your graduated cylinder to measure the volume of nutrient solution remaining in the reservoir of your growing system after 24 hours. Use this figure to determine the volume of water that passed into the reservoir. Record your data in the appropriate boxes on Student Sheet 10.3.

2. Replenish the nutrient solution and return the growing system to the plant light house.

3. Have a member of your group transfer your information to the transparency provided by your teacher.

4. When all groups have transferred their information to the transparency, add their data to your student sheet.

5. Plot each group's data on the graph on Student Sheet 10.3. Then answer the questions that follow the graph.

6. Work with your group to update the organism photo cards for *Lemna* and Wisconsin Fast Plants with new information from this lesson.

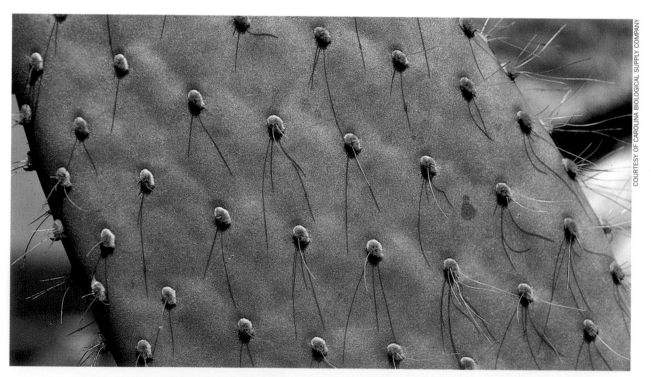

COURTESY OF CAROLINA BIOLOGICAL SUPPLY COMPANY

Figure 10.7 *Where are the leaves on this cactus plant? Why does this plant not need broad, flat leaves such as those on the Fast Plants?*

Figure 10.8 *This tree has leaves of many beautiful colors. Why do you think leaves change color in the fall in certain climates?*

REFLECTING ON WHAT YOU'VE DONE

Review "Looking at Leaves," the reading selection that follows. Respond to the following on your student sheets.

A. What evidence did you find that the lettuce you observed is a leaf?

B. What service does transpiration provide for plants?

C. What substances enter or exit a plant's leaves through the stomata?

D. Why do you think *Lemna* form their stomata in the upper epidermis?

E. Explain how guard cells operate to form a stoma.

F. Compare what happened to the guard cells in the model of the stomatal unit with what happened to the cells of the *Elodea* leaf that you observed soaking in salt solution during Lesson 7.

G. Use the graph on Student Sheet 10.3 to estimate the average volume of nutrient solution that passed from the reservoirs into the planters in 24 hours.

H. Use the graph to determine whether a relationship exists between the number of leaves on the Fast Plants and the volume of nutrient solution that entered the planter in 24 hours. Explain the relationship, if one exists.

I. Explain why you think the number of leaves on a plant would affect the amount of transpiration that occurs.

J. Describe two ways in which you think Wisconsin Fast Plants use the nutrient solution absorbed by their roots.

K. How does the control growing system help prove that most of the water escapes through the plant?

Looking at Leaves

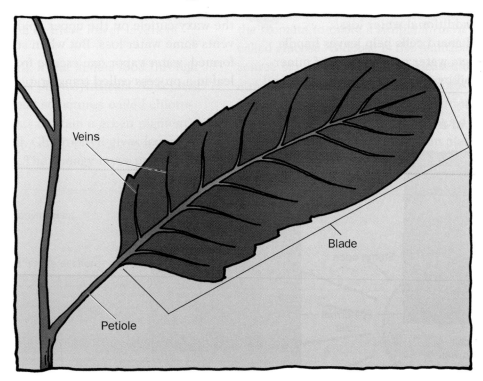

Veins

Blade

Petiole

If you live in a region with cold winters, you know what happens in spring. The air gets warmer; the days get longer. Green plants sprout in the garden and along roadsides. Everywhere you look outside, you see green as plants reveal their hidden treasures—leaves.

Leaves come in many shapes, sizes, and textures. But however different leaves may appear, their parts work in similar ways to accomplish their main task—making food for plants. Plants need food and water to survive and grow. Let's take a look at how the parts of a leaf work together to produce food and help regulate a plant's water content.

Parts You Can Easily See: Blades, Petioles, and Veins

What do you see when you look at a leaf? Most leaves have two basic parts: the blade and the petiole. The blade is usually broad and flat. The petiole is the narrow, stem-like part. It joins the blade to the stem or branch. You also might see the leaf's veins. Veins carry water and other substances throughout a plant.

Parts You Can't Easily See: Stomata and Guard Cells

The outer surface of a dicot leaf's blade is called the epidermis. It is a thin, tough layer of cells that covers both surfaces of the blade. The epidermis is the leaf's "skin." Its cells often secrete a waxy film, called a cuticle, which covers the upper epidermis. The cuticle protects the leaf from being injured and from losing too much water.

Scattered mostly throughout the lower epidermis of dicot leaves are tiny openings called stomata (the singular is stoma). How does a stoma form? The guard cells, a pair of sausage-shaped cells that lie against each other, take in

Exploring Microorganisms

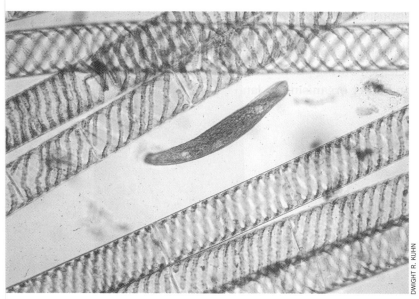

You'll often see a variety of organisms
in just one drop of water!

DWIGHT R. KUHN

INTRODUCTION

In Lesson 4, you created your own pond ecosystem. Soon you will revisit your pond to observe any new developments. This lesson will prepare you to make those observations. During this lesson, you will observe four types of microorganisms and decide whether their characteristics are more animal-like or plant-like. You also will draw and label the microorganisms and estimate their lengths. You will create a cartoon featuring one of the microorganisms you observe. You will learn about the effects that microorganisms have had on our world. Finally, you will read about a kingdom of organisms whose benefits to humans are often misunderstood—kingdom Monera.

OBJECTIVES FOR THIS LESSON

Make a list of things you already know about microorganisms.

Observe four species of living microorganisms called protists and identify their animal-like and plant-like characteristics.

Observe, draw, and estimate the length of four protists.

Create a cartoon using an *Amoeba, Euglena,* or *Paramecium* as the main character.

Read about the importance of microorganisms in history.

Read about the kingdom Monera and its significance to humans.

Update your organism photo cards for *Amoeba, Euglena,* and *Paramecium.*

THE FINE ART OF NAMING ORGANISMS

One of the first microorganisms that scientists viewed through a microscope was a squirmy little creature they named "amoeba." Latin and Greek were the languages used by scientists in the Western world at that time, late in the 17th century. The name "amoeba" is based on the Latin and Greek words for "to change." Scientists thought the name was appropriate because the amoeba's shape was always changing.

Although the meaning of *amoeba* is pretty straightforward, learning how to write the word properly can be confusing. For example, because the English language does not contain the Greek sound represented by the letters "oe," the English spelling of amoeba has never been consistent. Depending on what you are reading, you may see this word appear as *Amoeba, Amaeba, Ameba,* amoeba, or ameba!

Adding to the confusion is the fact that the genus name *Amoeba,* which is capitalized and italicized, has also become this organism's common name, amoeba, which is neither capitalized nor italicized. Furthermore, when talking about more than one of these microorganisms, some people use the Latin plural form, amoebae, but others use the English plural, amoebas.

(continued)

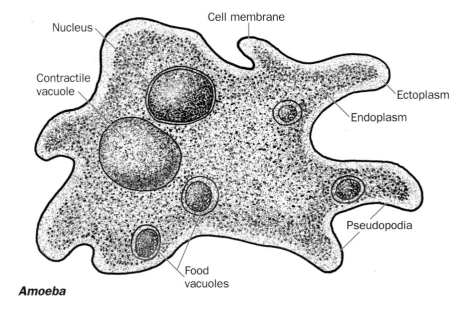

Amoeba

(continued)

Another microorganism named by early scientists was *Paramecium*. Because it is shaped like a slipper, they named it using the Greek word for "oval." People now use "paramecium" (no capital letter, no italics) as the common name for this organism. The most common plural form is "paramecia." Paramecia are found in fresh water around the world. They are among the most complex of all single-celled organisms.

A third freshwater organism named by early scientists seemed like a cross between an animal and a plant. Like many plants, it was bright green. But it moved like an animal, and it did not have a cell wall. Impressed by this microbe's ability to use its tiny eyespot to find the brightest areas in its environment, scientists gave it the scientific name *Euglena*, from the Greek words that mean "true pupil of the eye." *Euglena* is found in ponds and pools of water. It is especially common in waters rich in chemicals.

The twisting, turning spheres that scientists named *Volvox* (from the Latin verb "to roll") seemed part animal, part plant. For many years, scientists classified *Volvox* as an animal. *Volvox* and the other microorganisms described above are now classified in a group separate from plants and animals—the kingdom Protista. This kingdom includes a diverse lot of mostly single-celled, aquatic organisms that have a well-defined nucleus. Since these organisms are in the kingdom Protista, they are commonly referred to as "protists."

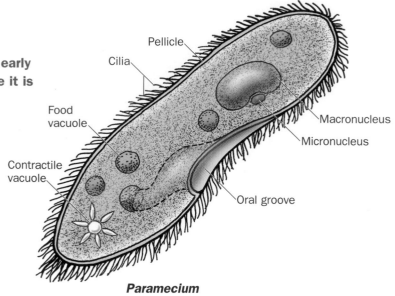

Pellicle
Cilia
Food vacuole
Macronucleus
Micronucleus
Contractile vacuole
Oral groove

Paramecium

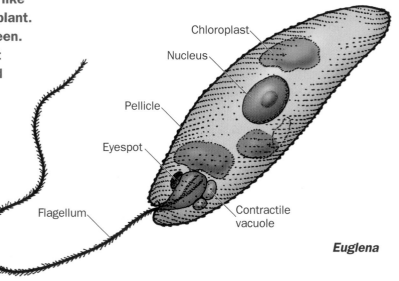

Chloroplast
Nucleus
Pellicle
Eyespot
Flagellum
Contractile vacuole

Euglena

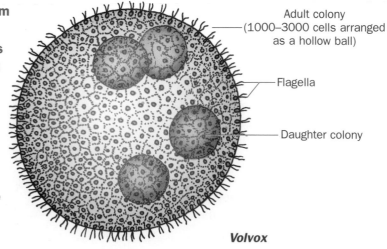

Adult colony (1000–3000 cells arranged as a hollow ball)
Flagella
Daughter colony

Volvox

Getting Started

1. With your group, list in your science notebook five things you already know about microorganisms.

2. Discuss your list with the class.

3. With your class, read the Introduction and "The Fine Art of Naming Organisms" at the beginning of this lesson.

MATERIALS FOR LESSON 11

For you

1 copy of Student Sheet 11.2: Template for Protist Drawings

1 box of colored pencils

For your group

2 copies of Inquiry Master 11.3B: Scoring Rubric for Protist Cartoons

1 set of organism photo cards

2 compound light microscopes

2 depression slides

2 coverslips

2 transparent rulers

2 metric rulers, 30 cm (12 in.)

8 strands of cotton

1 *Amoeba*

1 *Paramecium*

1 *Euglena*

1 *Volvox*

1 *Amoeba* slide

1 *Paramecium* slide

1 *Euglena* slide

1 *Volvox* slide

Inquiry 11.1
Exploring Living Protists

PROCEDURE

1. Take the following steps to obtain, observe, and record information about the four living protists your teacher has made available. You may observe the protists in any order you wish.

A. Have one student from your pair take a slide and coverslip to the center where your teacher has placed the containers of protists, the plastic pipettes, and cotton balls.

B. Place two or three strands of cotton in the depression on the slide. The cotton helps confine the protists to a smaller area.

C. Use a plastic pipette to obtain a sample of water from one of the culture containers. Check to see if there are any special instructions for obtaining the protists. The instructions will be on the label of the container or on a nearby card.

D. Transfer the protists to the slide by squeezing a single drop of water from the pipette into the slide's depression. Add a coverslip. Return to your seat and place the slide on the microscope stage.

E. With your partner, locate the protist under a magnification of 100×. If you cannot find the protist, clean your slide, then go back and obtain another drop of water. Center one of the protists in the field of view and switch to a magnification of 400×, as seen in Figure 11.1. If you cannot keep the microbe in the field of view under 400×, switch back to 100×.

F. Identify as many of the organelles as you can that are labeled in the illustrations in "The Fine Art of Naming Organisms."

Figure 11.1 *This student is using the fine adjustment knobs to focus on a microbe under high magnification.*

G. On a new page in your science notebook, create a table like Table 11.1 to record observations about the protists. Make your table the size of a full page.

H. Try to determine how the protist moves. Identify any structures that seem to help it move.

I. With your partner, decide which of the protist's features and behaviors are animal-like and which are plant-like. List these in the table.

J. When you have finished observing a protist, fill a plastic pipette with water from the appropriate culture container. Hold the slide over the water in the culture container while you use the plastic pipette to squirt the water from the container over the slide, as shown in Figure 11.2. This should wash the protists back into the culture container. Be careful not to allow cotton fibers to get into the container.

2. Rinse the slide and coverslip with tap water. Lay them on a dry paper towel and flip them over several times until they are dry. Continue working with the other protists until you are finished.

Figure 11.2 *Hold the slide over the culture container with one hand while squirting water over the top of the slide with a pipette in the other hand.*

Table 11.1 Observations of Microorganisms

Protist	Animal-like Features	Plant-like Features	Structures/Methods of Movement
Amoeba			
Paramecium			
Euglena			
Volvox			

Inquiry 11.2
Observing and Drawing Protists From Prepared Slides

PROCEDURE

1. Follow these steps to prepare scientific drawings from prepared slides of the four protists— *Amoeba, Paramecium, Euglena,* and *Volvox.*

Figure 11.3 *Students have different styles when working with the microscope. Notice that the microscope in this photo is in a different position than the one in Figure 11.1.*

A. Take turns with your partner to observe each of the four protists and draw each on Student Sheet 11.2: Template for Protist Drawings. Use the magnification that allows you to see the structures of the protist most clearly. You may draw the protists in any order.

B. Title each drawing with the appropriate name. Label all of the organelles you can identify. Use your metric ruler to draw the lines for labels. Follow all guidelines for scientific drawings.

C. As you did in Lesson 2, use the transparent ruler to measure the diameter of the field of view at both 100× and 400×. Use those measurements to help you estimate the length of each of the four protists. Record the estimated lengths in millimeters in the appropriate place on your student sheet.

D. As you complete each drawing, trade slides or switch seats with a pair of students that has finished using a slide of a different protist.

2. When you have completed your drawings, follow your teacher's directions for cleaning up.

3. With your group, update your organism photo cards for *Amoeba, Euglena,* and *Paramecium.* (Note that there is no organism photo card for *Volvox.*)

Inquiry 11.3
Creating a Protist Cartoon

PROCEDURE

1. Create a cartoon with either an *Amoeba, Euglena,* or *Paramecium* as the central character.

2. Your cartoon must be accurately drawn and should show details of at least four organelles, such as flagella, cilia, pseudopods, nuclei, vacuoles, cell membranes (or pellicles), contractile vacuoles, oral grooves, and eyespots (stigmas).

3. Make your caption humorous, focusing on at least one major characteristic of the protist.

4. Make a draft copy in pencil; use colored pencils for your final version. You will complete this assignment at home. If available, you may use a computer to create a background and labels for your final cartoon.

5. Your teacher will tell you when your cartoon is due. Use the rubric in Table 11.2 to evaluate your cartoon before you turn it in. Your teacher will use this rubric, or one similar to it, to assess your work and will inform you of the point values for each box within the rubric.

Table 11.2 Scoring Rubric for Protist Cartoon

Requirements	Exemplary (Pts.)	Satisfactory (Pts.)	Needs Improvement (Pts.)	No Attempt (Pts.)
Cartoon clearly shows which protist is featured.				
At least four organelles are drawn accurately.				
Caption contains information about at least one feature of the protist.				
The caption, although humorous, is based on accurate information.				
Cartoon is neatly done and suitable for posting.				
			Total Points =	

REFLECTING ON WHAT YOU'VE DONE

1. On the basis of what you have learned in this lesson, respond to the following in your science notebook:

   A. What are some of the characteristics you noticed while observing the four protists?

   B. Why do you think these protists are not classified as animals or plants?

2. Revisit the list you developed during "Getting Started." Discuss with your group what should be revised.

3. Based on what you learned in the reading selections "Mighty Microbes" and "Welcome to the Monera Kingdom!" answer the following questions in your science notebook:

   C. Why is the misuse of antibacterial products and antibiotics potentially dangerous?

   D. What are at least four ways in which microorganisms are beneficial to humans?

WELCOME TO THE MONERA KINGDOM!

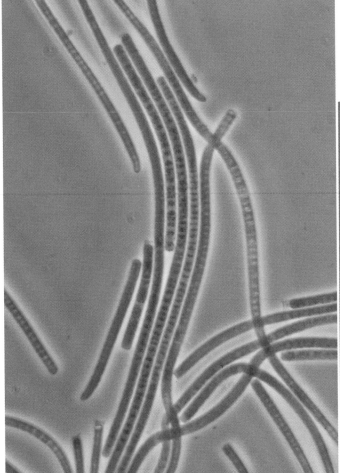

Oscillatoria

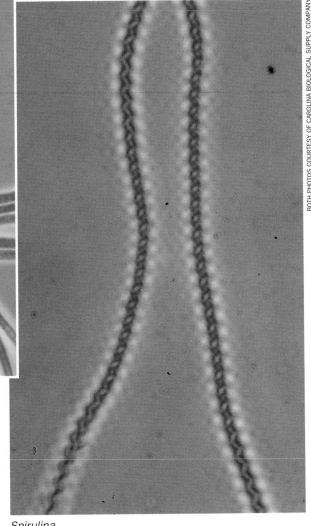

Spirulina

No, the Monera kingdom isn't some faraway territory ruled by a king and queen. It's a fairly recent classification of life form. To belong to the Monera kingdom, an organism has to be missing something that's found in all other life forms: a nuclear membrane which encloses an organism's genetic material, or DNA.

Bacteria, a large group of one-celled organisms found all over the planet, belong to the Monera kingdom. Organisms previously classified as blue-green algae, such as *Oscillatoria* and *Spirulina*, also are monerans because scientists have found that they are more similar to bacteria than to algae. Some scientists also place viruses in the Monera kingdom, because they, too, lack a membrane around their nucleus.

(continued)

There's No Escape!

But bacteria are the Monera kingdom's real claim to fame.

You can't get away from bacteria. They're everywhere—in the soil, air, and water. They're also in plants and animals. Without a microscope, you can't see individual bacteria cells. Yet despite their small size, bacteria aren't all alike. There are three main types, distinguished by their different shapes— rod, spiral, and spherical.

Rod

Spiral

Spherical

We all know that certain bacteria (often called "germs") can make us sick. For example, strep throat is caused by a bacterium called *Streptococcus.* Because of this and their very small size, bacteria aren't normally used as specimens in middle-school classrooms. To see bacteria in detail requires much more powerful microscopes, such as electron microscopes.

Did you also know that there are many more harmless—and even beneficial—bacteria than there are harmful ones? That's right! Some kinds of bacteria live in our digestive system. They help us process our food. Some of the intestinal gas we find so offensive forms when bacteria feed on undigested waste in our large intestine.

Another kind of bacteria lives in the roots of peas, beans, and other plants. These bacteria help put nitrogen into the soil. Without nitrogen, many plants would not survive.

So, don't think of bacteria as lowly members of the Monera kingdom. They perform many useful jobs. What's more, for about 2 billion years, they were the only life form on Earth. Once upon a time, bacteria ruled! Because they are so numerous and powerful, many people think they still do. ☐

MILOS KALAB

The small knobby spheres on the root of this pea plant contain bacteria that fix nitrogen the plant can use.

MIGHTY MICROBES

Dr. Leleng Isaacs (left) in her lab with students at Goucher College

It's hard to believe that something visible only through a microscope could change the course of history. But it's true—and that something is microbes.

Microbes are tiny organisms that live in the air, in water, and on just about any surface. According to Dr. Leleng Isaacs, microbes have shaped the history of Earth and of human beings.

Dr. Isaacs is a microbiologist—a scientist who studies tiny life forms. She has been studying microbes for many years and is writing a book about their impact on history. She and other scientists agree that humans are alive today because of microbes.

Microbes: The First Life Forms

When Earth was very young, the only life forms were microbes. They were invisible to the naked eye. But, Dr. Isaacs says, being invisible did not keep them from being very creative. For instance, scientists believe that one type of microbe, a blue-green alga, was the first to undergo photosynthesis. These algae used energy from the Sun to produce glucose from carbon dioxide and water. Glucose provides plants with the sources of energy they need to perform life activities. As glucose was formed by these early algae, oxygen was released into Earth's atmosphere.

(continued)

According to Dr. Isaacs, in a way, microbes also were the first polluters, and oxygen was the first pollutant. But in this case, polluting was a good thing. The oxygen that was released into the atmosphere helped create the ozone layer. That layer protects Earth from dangerous radiation. Without it, new life forms—including humans—could not have evolved.

Bad Microbes, Good Microbes

Some microbes cause diseases that can kill entire populations. This is particularly apt to happen when microbes are carried into a new area whose inhabitants have had no exposure to the disease. For example, when Europeans first came to the Western Hemisphere, they brought diseases that had existed in Europe for a long time but which had not been present in the Americas. Some of those diseases, such as smallpox, infected the native peoples living in North and South America. Many natives died because they had no immunity to those diseases. Microbes helped to wipe out mighty civilizations such as the Incas.

Today, we see similar threats from microbes. The human immunodeficiency virus (HIV), for instance, has infected hundreds of millions of people around the world. The disease it causes, acquired immune deficiency syndrome (AIDS), is spreading fast. Scientists are working hard to find a vaccine that will prevent AIDS.

At the same time, microbes can do a lot of good. Many antibiotics are made from bacteria and other microbes. You probably have taken penicillin or amoxicillin when you have had strep throat. Those medicines are made

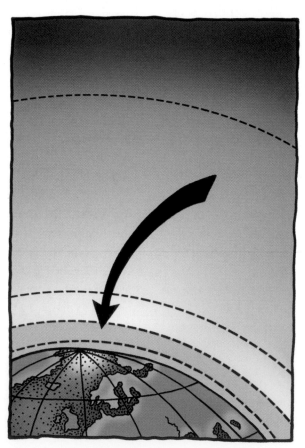

This 15-km layer of ozone, indicated by the arrow, helps protect us from the harmful rays of the Sun. (The Earth and the layers of atmosphere are not drawn to scale.)

Penicillin, discovered in a mold called Penicillium *by Alexander Fleming in 1928, was called the first wonder drug.*

from mold, a type of fungus. Before the discovery of antibiotics in 1928, thousands of people died every year from diseases caused by bacteria.

Too Much of a Good Thing

In TV ads, makers of soap and cleaning products brag that their products are "antibacterial." They say that's a good thing. Dr. Isaacs disagrees. She says overuse of antibacterial products and antibiotics is actually dangerous. Microbes can quickly become resistant to them. Then, scientists have to struggle to find newer, more effective medicines. Dr. Isaacs's advice? Use good old soap and water.

For Dr. Leleng Isaacs, microbiology is a fascinating field of study. Microbes are always changing and creating new challenges for scientists. She urges you to look into a microscope and discover the exciting world of microbes. □

12
Revisiting Your Pond

What stage in the life of a pond does this photo represent?

STEPHEN G. MAKA PHOTOGRAPHY

INTRODUCTION

In Lesson 4, you observed and sketched the layers of your pond and observed its water through a microscope. In this lesson, you will take another look at your pond to see what changes, if any, have occurred. You also will read "The Changing Pond" at the end of this lesson to find out how ponds develop and change over time in a natural setting.

OBJECTIVES FOR THIS LESSON

Observe your pond, then sketch it and label the living and nonliving things you included in your sketch.

Look for evidence of succession in your pond.

Use a compound microscope to observe, draw, and identify microorganisms from different depths in your pond.

Determine the average daily increase in the number of *Lemna* fronds over 3 weeks.

Getting Started

1. Do not shake or stir your pond.

2. With your group, take turns using the hand lenses to observe your pond at eye level. Make sure there is enough light to see into it clearly.

3. Compare your pond with the one you drew on Student Sheet 4.2. In your science notebook, list two ways in which your pond has changed and two ways in which it has remained the same.

4. Discuss your responses with the class.

MATERIALS FOR LESSON 12

For you

- 1 copy of Student Sheet 12.1A: My Pond and Its Organisms
- 1 copy of Student Sheet 12.2: Average Daily Increase in the Number of *Lemna* Fronds
- 1 copy of Student Sheet 4.2: Sketches of Pond—Macro and Micro

For your group

- 1 copy of Student Sheet 12.1B: Common Freshwater Microorganisms
- 1 pond (from Lesson 4)
- 2 compound light microscopes
- 2 depression slides
- 2 hand lenses
- 2 coverslips
- 2 plastic pipettes
- 1 small cotton ball
- 1 black marker
- 2 metric rulers, 30 cm (12 in.)

Inquiry 12.1
Observing and Drawing My Pond and Its Microbes

PROCEDURE

1. Sketch your pond in the box at the top of Student Sheet 12.1A: My Pond and Its Organisms. Include everything you can see, such as distinct layers and any organisms visible through a hand lens. Label the nonliving and living things.

2. Add a few strands of cotton to the depression on your slide.

3. Use a pipette to obtain water from an area near the surface of your pond. Add one drop to the cotton on the slide. Place a coverslip on the slide.

4. Focus on the drop of water under a magnification of 100×. While looking through the eyepiece, slowly move the slide around to locate microorganisms. Be sure to look for algae and other vegetation as well as mobile microbes.

5. Sketch as many of the organisms as you can in the circles provided on Student Sheet 12.1A. Follow the guidelines for scientific drawings. Change magnifications as needed, using whichever magnification gives the best view of each organism.

6. Repeat Step 5 with water samples taken carefully from the bottom level of your pond. On Student Sheet 12.1A, draw and label each new organism that you observe. Obtain another copy of Student Sheet 12.1A if you need more than four circles. Use Student Sheet 12.1B: Common Freshwater Microorganisms to help you identify unfamiliar microorganisms.

7. Share your slides with other students, especially if you find something particularly interesting.

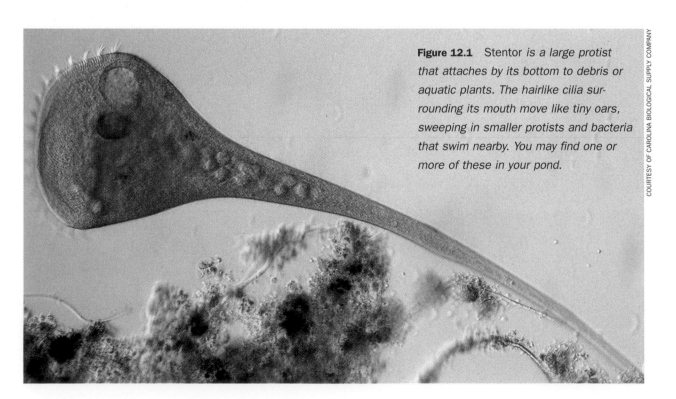

Figure 12.1 *Stentor is a large protist that attaches by its bottom to debris or aquatic plants. The hairlike cilia surrounding its mouth move like tiny oars, sweeping in smaller protists and bacteria that swim nearby. You may find one or more of these in your pond.*

COURTESY OF CAROLINA BIOLOGICAL SUPPLY COMPANY

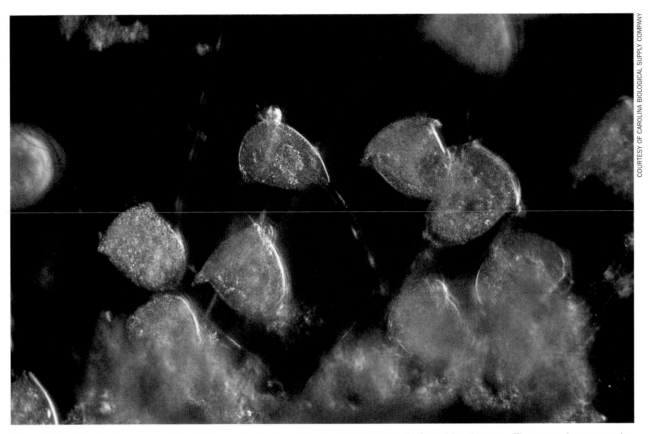

COURTESY OF CAROLINA BIOLOGICAL SUPPLY COMPANY

Figure 12.2 Vorticella *are protists that can live independently but are usually found in clusters. They attach to aquatic plants using a stalk that contracts like a spring when disturbed. Can you find one in your pond?*

Figure 12.3 Pediastrum *are green protists that live in colonies of 32–64 cells. They can usually be found at the edge of a pond, below the top layer of sand and soil.*

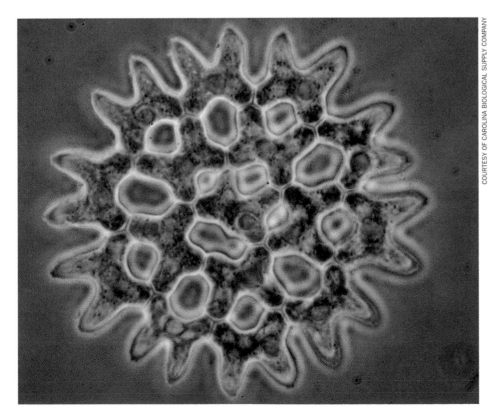

COURTESY OF CAROLINA BIOLOGICAL SUPPLY COMPANY

The Changing Pond

MICHAEL P. GADOMSKI/THE NATIONAL AUDOBON SOCIETY COLLECTION/PHOTO RESEARCHERS, INC.

Think about the day you created your pond and the substances that you added to the cup. They included gravel, soil, decaying leaves, straw, rice grains, water, and *Lemna*. When you observed water from your pond through a microscope on that day, you probably saw little evidence of living organisms.

Now that your pond is older, it looks quite different. Of course, your pond wasn't created in the same way that ponds are created in nature. Natural ponds are just shallow depressions where water has collected. They are usually no more than 3–4 meters deep, and sunlight can reach their bottoms.

As they age, natural ponds go through a gradual process of change known as succession. First, a depression fills with water, attracting nearby wildlife. Land animals and birds that come to inhabit the area bring in plant seeds and spores. Seeds and spores also may blow or drift in. Over time, plants grow from the seeds, and vegetation in and around the pond increases. Some types of plants float on the surface; others grow on the bottom. Still other types of vegetation grow on the banks of the pond.

In addition, wind and rain can carry decaying leaves, straw, and soil into ponds. (In your pond, you added the straw, leaves, and soil.) Microbes are often attached to these substances. Many of these microbes—particularly protists—form an envelope, called a cyst, around themselves for protection against unfavorable environmental conditions such as cold or hot temperatures or dryness. When they are carried into ponds and exposed to water and suitable temperatures, the microbes are revived. The cysts wear away, and the microbes resume their normal life activities.

Over many years, as each type of vegetation in a pond dies and decomposes, plant debris accumulates at the pond's bottom. Animals die and their remains also fall to the bottom of the pond. The mixture of materials is called "detritus." The dead plant and animal material

Succession of a pond

provide nourishment for organisms called decomposers—bacteria, fungi, certain types of insects, and worms. These organisms thrive on organic matter. Eventually, the products of decomposition fill up the pond. The "bottom" of the pond literally rises close to the top!

At this point, plants root in the decomposed matter at the bottom and send their leaves into the air. The pond becomes a marsh or swamp. As the area continues to fill in, trees begin to grow in the water. Over a long time, the pond fills in and slowly dries out, becoming either a forest or a grassland, depending on the local climate.

The pond has completed its succession. It is now considered a "climax community." This is a stable community in which the numbers and types of organisms are in relative balance. Unless a major disturbance occurs, succession will cease. ☐

A Pond's Hidden Life

Life in a pond is not always obvious. The most important sources of food for all organisms in a pond are microbes. In addition to being food sources, many microbes, such as algae, release oxygen needed by other organisms in the water. Larger, floating, rooted, and submerged plants also contribute to the food supply.

There are many food chains and food webs in a pond ecosystem. Microscopic meat eaters (carnivores) feed on microscopic plant eaters (herbivores), which feed on algae and other types of tiny, plant-like organisms. Predatory insects in and around a pond feed on microscopic carnivores. These insects are eaten by larger insects and spiders, which in turn, may be eaten by birds, frogs, fish, and other animals. These organisms will have been attracted to the pond by the food and shelter this habitat offers.

Look again at your pond. What do you think it will look like after more time passes?

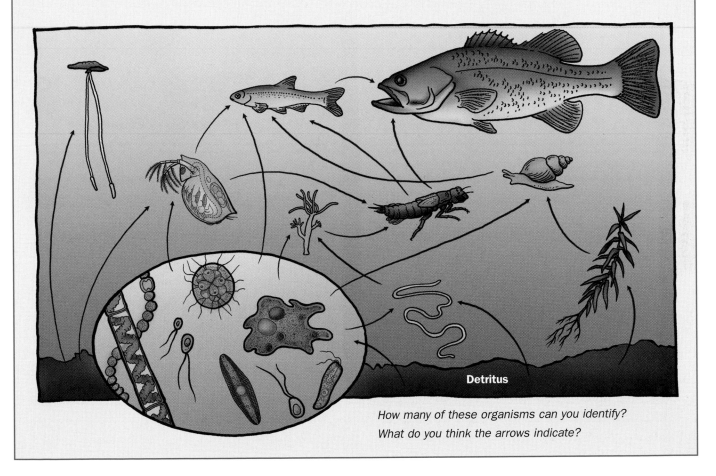

Detritus

How many of these organisms can you identify?
What do you think the arrows indicate?

PART 3 Completing the Cycle

LESSON 13
Anchor Activity

This bat-eating snake is capable of swallowing creatures twice its diameter.

How long would you last lying on the ice with no clothes for protection?

INTRODUCTION

Did you ever wonder how a snake can devour things more than twice its diameter? Or how a seal keeps from freezing in subzero temperatures? In this lesson, you will work with your group to explore what constitutes a habitat and to investigate a vertebrate—an animal with a backbone—such as that snake or seal. Your group then will divide into pairs. One pair will investigate how the vertebrate's body structure affects various aspects of its life, from what it eats and how it gets its food, to how it interacts with its own species and others. The other pair of students will research the vertebrate's habitat. Your group will work as a team to present your findings to the class. Your teacher will discuss the options for presenting your final product. You also will read a true story about an organism called *Daphnia* and its connections to Charles Darwin and his theory of evolution.

OBJECTIVES FOR THIS LESSON

Read about factors that determine where an organism lives.

Select a vertebrate and research how the structure of its body parts influences the way those parts function.

Research your vertebrate's habitat to discover the biotic and abiotic factors that might affect its ability to survive.

Share your findings with the class using a presentation method approved by your teacher.

Read about an organism called *Daphnia* and decide whether its rapid evolution supports Charles Darwin's ideas.

Getting Started

1. Read silently as a classmate reads aloud the Introduction to this lesson.

2. Watch the videotape *Body by Design: Form and Function* and take notes based on your teacher's instructions.

3. Brainstorm with your group a list of vertebrate body parts with unique adaptations for performing one or more functions.

4. Share your list with the class.

Inquiry 13.1
Introducing the Research Project

ANCHOR ACTIVITY

1. Listen while your teacher introduces the Anchor Activity, including appropriate research methods, reference requirements, deadlines, and presentation formats. Follow along as your teacher reviews Student Sheet 13.1: Anchor Activity Schedule and Table 13.1: Anchor Activity Scoring Rubric. Your teacher will tell you the appropriate point values for each part of the scoring rubric.

2. Follow along while students take turns reading "Habitats" at the end of this lesson to find out more about habitats in general.

MATERIALS

For you
1 copy of Student Sheet 13.1: Anchor Activity Schedule

For each group of 4 students
1 copy of Inquiry Master 13.1: Lists of Vertebrates

Choosing a Vertebrate

1. Work with your group to choose a vertebrate to research. Refer to a variety of sources including the lists provided by your teacher, your school media center, and your own resources.

2. Obtain your teacher's approval for your group's final choice.

3. Decide which pair from your group will research how your vertebrate's various body parts are suited to their functions and which pair will research the vertebrate's habitat.

ANIMALS WITH BACKBONES

A vertebrate is an organism with a backbone. Vertebrates are grouped within the phylum Chordata of the Animal kingdom and are further separated into five major classes:

Class Mammalia—Warm-blooded animals with hair or fur and mammary glands

This brown bear, with its thick coat of fur, is a rugged specimen of a mammal.

Class Aves—Warm-blooded animals with feathers and hollow bones

These waxed albatrosses are warm-blooded, which means that their bodies maintain a constant internal body temperature. What do you think "cold-blooded" means?

Class Reptilia—Cold-blooded animals with scales that lay their eggs on land

This snake has a threatening rattle that wards off enemies.

Class Amphibia—Cold-blooded animals that live part of their life in water and part on land (they breathe by means of gills when young, but develop lungs as adults); they lay their eggs in water

This leopard frog is well camouflaged amidst the duckweed. The position of its eyes allows it to observe its surroundings without exposing its whole body to predators.

Class Pisces—Cold-blooded animals that live in water (they are often divided into smaller groups, such as jawless fish, cartilage fish, and bony fish)

This green sunfish is just one of many species of sunfish you might find in a pond or lake.

Table 13.1 Anchor Activity Scoring Rubric

Quality of Content on Vertebrate Form and Function	Points Possible
Final product displays exemplary coverage of at least 5 vertebrate structures and their functions. Research and references exceed the minimum requirements.	
Final product displays above-average coverage of at least 5 vertebrate structures and their functions. Research and references are above average.	
Final product displays satisfactory coverage of at least 5 vertebrate structures and their functions. Research and references are sufficient.	
Final product displays below-average coverage of at least 5 vertebrate structures and their functions. Research and references are insufficient.	
Final product displays limited or no coverage of vertebrate structures and functions. Few or no sources of information are evident.	

OR

Quality of Content on Vertebrate Habitat	Points Possible
Final product displays exemplary coverage of biotic and abiotic factors in the vertebrate's habitat. Research, visuals, and references exceed the minimum requirements.	
Final product displays above-average coverage of biotic and abiotic factors in the vertebrate's habitat. Research, visuals, and references are above average.	
Final product displays satisfactory coverage of biotic and abiotic factors in the vertebrate's habitat. Research, visuals, and references are sufficient.	
Final product displays below-average coverage of the biotic and abiotic factors in the vertebrate's habitat. Research and references are insufficient.	
Final product displays limited or no coverage of the biotic and abiotic factors in the vertebrate's habitat. Few or no sources of information are evident.	

AND

Presentation Design and Appearance	Points Possible
Final product clearly, effectively, and creatively displays the main ideas. It is well organized and attractive.	
Final product clearly and effectively displays the main ideas. It is organized and relatively attractive.	
Final product communicates some of the main ideas but is lacking in organization and structure. The appearance is satisfactory.	
Final product ineffectively communicates the main ideas, lacks detail and structure, and is unorganized and unattractive.	

Table 13.1 Anchor Activity Scoring Rubric (continued)

Presentation to Class	Points Possible
Presenter clearly, effectively, and creatively communicated the required information in a style appropriate for the audience.	
Presenter clearly and effectively communicated the required information in a style appropriate for the audience.	
Presenter communicated some of the required information, but presentation lacked some detail, organization, and structure.	
Presenter ineffectively communicated the required information; the presentation lacked considerable detail, organization, and structure.	

REFLECTING ON WHAT YOU'VE DONE

Read the following passage about Charles Darwin and the article entitled "*Daphnia*'s Change of Appetite." Then write a minimum of 150 words explaining which of Darwin's ideas are addressed in the reading selection and how those ideas are supported. Turn in your work to your teacher by the date requested in the schedule provided on Student Sheet 13.1.

Charles Darwin and His Theory of Evolution

In 1859, British naturalist Charles Darwin published his groundbreaking book, *Origin of Species*. In this remarkable book, Darwin explained his theory of evolution, which was based on many years of observations. The book illustrated several important points:

- Many variations exist within species. For example, some humans are taller than others; some giraffes have longer necks than others.
- All organisms compete for the resources they need to survive.
- Organisms can produce more offspring than can survive given the quantity of resources available.
- Organisms that are fit and better able to deal with changes in their environment tend to survive and reproduce, passing their desirable traits on to their offspring. This is known as "natural selection," or "survival of the fittest."

Charles Darwin

Daphnia's Change of Appetite

Have you ever thrown away something you were about to eat because it did not smell right? Or dumped milk down the drain because it seemed spoiled? If so, you probably did the right thing. Eating or drinking food that has spoiled can make you sick.

But what if *all* your food turned bad and you had nothing else to eat? If your body would not accept the bad food, you would starve. In the natural world, many creatures face this problem. This is especially true of organisms that live in lakes close to cities and towns, where pollution often is a problem.

Pollution from human activity has gradually poisoned the food of many aquatic, or water-dwelling, organisms. Because these organisms live within confined bodies of water, they can't leave their homes to seek cleaner waters. If none of the organisms is able to survive the pollution, the entire species will perish in that habitat.

What's for Dinner?

In Lake Constance in Germany, one tiny creature has defied the odds. It is called *Daphnia,* and it belongs to a biological class called Crustacea. The best-known crustaceans are shrimp, crabs, and lobsters. *Daphnia* is much smaller than any of these. You might call it a "shrimp's shrimp."

Since 1970, human-caused pollution in Lake Constance has killed off much of *Daphnia*'s

Pollution often limits the types of organisms that are able to survive in a lake or pond.

one-time favorite food—harmless green algae. While the green algae could not survive the pollution, a different species, a poisonous blue-green form of algae called *Cyanobacteria,* flourished. It now dominates the lake. *Cyanobacteria* is not only dangerous to

Daphnia; humans also can get very sick if they drink water containing these algae.

After the harmless green algae were gone, *Daphnia* in Lake Constance turned to the other available source of food—the dangerous *Cyanobacteria.* Surprisingly, the entire population of *Daphnia* did not die off. Those rare *Daphnia* endowed with genes that allowed them to tolerate the new diet of *Cyanobacteria* survived, reproduced, and passed on their tolerance

(continued)

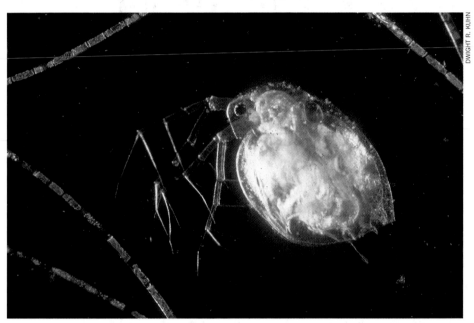

Daphnia *illuminated in a drop of water swimming among the algal filaments*

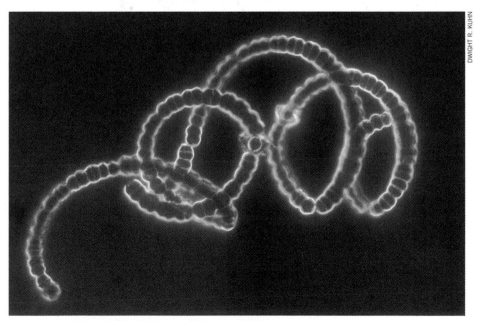

This harmless-looking organism, a type of Cyanobacteria, *can be very harmful to most* Daphnia.

The older Daphnia *eggs are buried deeper in the lake's bottom.*

to their offspring. If there had been no *Daphnia* with this tolerance in Lake Constance, their species in the lake would have perished.

New *Daphnia* From Old Eggs

How do scientists know that *Daphnia* have evolved? Through an amazing bit of detective work.

Scientists knew that each year, after *Daphnia* laid their eggs, some of the eggs became buried at the bottom of Lake Constance. Year after year, the sediment covered more and more eggs. So the deeper the eggs are buried, the older they are.

A group of scientists decided to dig up some eggs that had been buried about 30 years ago, before the lake became polluted, as well as some eggs that were buried about 20 years ago. Then

the scientists brought the eggs to the laboratory, where, incredibly, the 30-year-old eggs were still able to hatch! They raised the newly hatched *Daphnia* in the laboratory, feeding deadly *Cyanobacteria* to both the pre- and post-pollution creatures.

What did the scientists discover? *Daphnia* from the older eggs couldn't eat *Cyanobacteria* and survive. Their diet evidently had been the green algae, and they couldn't "stomach" the blue-green stuff. And—you guessed it—*Daphnia* hatched from 20-year-old eggs ate the toxic blue-green algae without a problem!

The scientists were surprised. *Daphnia* had evolved in only about 10 years. In the process, the species had survived in the lake, and, by consuming the poisonous *Cyanobacteria,* had helped make Lake Constance safe for humans again. ☐

Habitats

This fungus lives very comfortably on and within this tree.

A habitat is any place where a plant or animal lives. A habitat can be a desert for a cactus or a rattlesnake, an ocean for a whale or a sea turtle, a grassland for a bison or a gazelle, or a rainforest for a monkey or a rubber tree. A habitat can be an animal's intestine, as it is for some parasitic worms. A habitat can be a single tree, as it is for some species of fungi.

The concept of a habitat is quite simple. It is an organism's home. It is a place that supplies an organism with all it needs—food, water, shelter, and a place to bear and raise its young.

The reality of habitats, however, is not so simple. Consider the sea turtle, for example. Females of the world's seven sea turtle species all come to shore to nest and lay their eggs. When the babies hatch, they rush to the sea, which becomes their habitat. But for a very brief time in the female sea turtle's life, the ocean shore becomes its habitat. Male sea turtles never

(continued)

need to return to land. So for adult males, the ocean becomes their only habitat.

Within the vast ocean, sea turtles find different types of habitats. Some leatherback sea turtles spend part of the year in Alaskan waters, feeding on jelly-fish. Hawksbill turtles feed along tropical coral reefs, while young Kemp's Ridley sea turtles mature in the reefs of the Sargasso Sea.

Of all the hatchlings that now call the ocean their home, only the females eventually will return to land to lay their eggs.

Salmon alternate between two different habitats and, like the female sea turtle, must have both for their species to survive. Salmon hatch in freshwater streams and migrate to the sea, where they live for a few years before swimming back up the streams of their birth to lay eggs and die.

Through the process of evolution, many plants and animals change in ways that make certain habitats threatening to their survival. Some species have adapted to very specific food requirements and therefore are limited to habitats where that food is available. Australia's koala bear, for example, feeds only on the leaves of a few species of eucalyptus trees, making it highly specialized. Species like the koala are often very vulnerable to changes in their habitat. If disease were to kill off Australia's

These salmon struggle to swim upstream to their spawning grounds.

eucalyptus trees, for example, the koala in that area would soon perish. By contrast, for their survival, cabbage white butterflies depend on plants in the mustard family, which include more than 3000 species in over 300 genera. Therefore, the cabbage white may inhabit the many places in the world in which varieties of mustard plants are found.

Vertebrates in two classes, mammals and birds, are warm-blooded. This means that they maintain a constant body temperature. The other three classes of vertebrates—reptiles, amphibians, and fish—consist of animals that are cold-blooded, meaning that they take on the temperature of their surroundings. Because they can maintain a constant body temperature, mammals and birds are generally able to adapt to a wider range of temperatures and thus a wider range of habitats.

It is important to understand that evolution of a species happens entirely by chance. Evolution does not occur in order to help organisms adapt to a habitat. If a species cannot adapt to protect itself in some way from changes that occur within its habitat, it is left with two alternatives. It may move to a more suitable habitat, or it may become extinct. And finding a suitable habitat isn't always easy. In fact, scientists estimate that more than 99 percent of all the species of organisms that have ever lived are now extinct.

Some organisms, such as certain species of mammals, birds, and fish, migrate to other areas during certain times of the year to follow the food supply, to seek more suitable temperatures, to reproduce, or for a combination of these reasons. As a result, their habitats temporarily change. Other organisms have avoidance strategies to cope with changes in their environment. For example, some microorganisms form spores or cysts, encasing themselves within thick, durable coverings to protect themselves from the elements. Seeds may go into periods of rest, or dormancy. The cabbage white butterfly larva forms a protective chrysalis, a stage of metamorphosis in which it

may exist until conditions are favorable for it to emerge as an adult.

A habitat may be as tiny as a drop of water or a pinch of soil or as large as an ocean or a forest as long as it provides an organism those things it needs for its survival—food, shelter, and a place to reproduce. ☐

CORBIS/ROYALTY-FREE

This koala is resting comfortably on the branches of a eucalyptus tree, the leaves of which are its main diet.

Investigating Fungi I—The Molds

Fungi come in many shapes and sizes. Here is one example.

© BRIAN KUHN/DWIGHT KUHN PHOTOGRAPHY

INTRODUCTION

What do you think of when you hear the term *fungus?* Does it conjure up a positive image in your mind? Or is it something you normally associate with things that aren't so pleasant? Actually, fungi (the plural of fungus) are very important to us in many ways. In this lesson and the next, you will explore the nature of fungi and the important role they play in our lives.

OBJECTIVES FOR THIS LESSON

Observe a photo of "mystery prints" and agree on how they were formed.

Decide on conditions favorable for the formation of mold.

Compare the rate of mold formation on two types of bread.

Observe and document the progress of a fungal garden.

Read about the structure of bread mold and the nature of fungi in general.

Update the bread mold organism photo card.

Getting Started

1. With your group, observe Figure 14.1. It contains a "mystery print" left on a piece of paper by a living organism that is probably familiar to most of you. Agree on the type of organism that left the print and how the print was formed. List this information in your science notebook.

2. Share your ideas with the class while your teacher records your responses.

3. Agree on three conditions you think would be favorable for the growth of mold and list them in your science notebook.

4. Share your ideas with the class. As a class, narrow your ideas to the three most favorable conditions. Next, identify places in your classroom where these conditions are most likely to exist.

MATERIALS FOR LESSON 14

For your group

1 copy of Student Sheet 14.1: Comparing Mold Formation on Two Types of Bread
1 set of organism photo cards
2 small resealable plastic bags
¼ slice of brand-name bread
¼ slice of freshly baked bread
½ paper towel
1 pair of scissors
2 hand lenses
1 plastic pipette
1 black marker
  Transparent tape
  Tap water

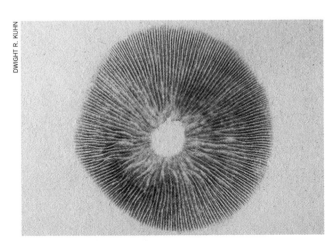

DWIGHT R. KUHN

Figure 14.1 *Mystery print*

Inquiry 14.1
Comparing Mold Formation on Two Types of Bread

PROCEDURE

1. On the outline on Student Sheet 14.1, design an inquiry to investigate whether brand-name bread or freshly baked bread will show evidence of mold more rapidly when placed in a suitable location in the classroom. You may choose your equipment from the materials list. You also may request additional items from your teacher.

2. While designing your inquiry, discuss and agree on what the inquiry should include in order to yield valid results. Consider the following questions:

   How will you ensure that both types of bread are kept under the same conditions?

   What kind of results are you looking for and how will you measure them?

Mold helps decompose organic matter, such as this dead cricket.

How often will you check your bread and record your observations?

How and where will you record your observations?

What items of equipment will you need?

How will you distinguish your bread from that of other groups in your class?

How will you communicate your results to the rest of the class?

What will you do to make sure your inquiry meets the safety requirements for handling moldy substances?

3. Include in your inquiry design a list of at least four things that you will keep constant in your inquiry.

4. Set up your materials for the inquiry. Return any unused equipment to your teacher.

SAFETY TIPS

When culturing live organisms, such as mold, always keep them in a sealed container.

Return all sealed plastic bags containing mold to your teacher for disposal.

Wash your hands after handling moldy food.

Inquiry 14.2
Creating and Observing a Fungal Garden

PROCEDURE

1. Your teacher has placed in your classroom a plastic container filled with food brought in by volunteers. Observe the container's contents every 2 days for evidence of mold.

2. Follow your teacher's directions for recording your observations of the container's contents in your science notebook until he or she tells you it is no longer necessary. Include such things as:

- *the date each of the foods first showed signs of molding*
- *whether there are different kinds of mold in the container*
- *whether there are signs of organisms other than mold in the container*

REFLECTING ON WHAT YOU'VE DONE

1. Answer the following questions in your science notebook. For assistance, refer to the reading selection "There's a Fungus Among Us" at the end of this lesson.

A. Which of the two bread samples first showed signs of molding? How do you account for this?

Watch out for Amanita! *It's one of the world's most beautiful fungi, but it can be deadly if eaten.*

B. Why do you think fungal inhibitors are added to bread if the bread will mold anyway?

C. Explain why bread mold may be present on a piece of bread well before you might notice it.

D. Were the room conditions you chose the best for mold formation? Did you prove this? How?

E. Was there more than one species of mold in your fungal garden? How could you tell?

F. Most fungi are "decomposers." What does this term mean, and why are decomposers so important to us? How does this relate to what happened in the fungal garden?

G. Why do different kinds of food items decompose at different rates?

2. Visit the STC/MS™ Web site (http://www.stcms.si.edu) and follow the links to learn more about the Fungi kingdom.

It's easy to see how this bird's nest fungus got its name. Actually the "eggs" are masses of spores that splash out of the "nest" when bombarded by a raindrop.

COURTESY OF CAROLINA BIOLOGICAL SUPPLY COMPANY

There's a Fungus Among Us

Fungi are strange organisms. Unlike animals, they can't capture their own food. And unlike plants, they can't make food from sunlight. Most can't even move around.

But fungi are hardy organisms. They are found almost everywhere. Some are deadly if eaten, but they also can play a positive role in cleaning up our environment.

What Belongs in the Fungi Kingdom?

The Fungi kingdom is huge. Some scientists estimate there are as many as 1.5 million species of

(continued)

There is an amazing variety of species in the Fungi kingdom. The structures we are able to see are usually the reproductive ones.

15

Investigating Fungi II—Yeast

What do you think this photo has to do with the topic of this lesson?

INTRODUCTION

In this lesson, you will focus on another member of the Fungi kingdom—yeast. You may have heard of yeast being added to bread or cake dough to make it rise. But did you know that yeast cells are living organisms? In this lesson, you will observe a yeast culture and watch as evidence of an important life process bubbles up before your eyes. You will design an inquiry to investigate substances that affect yeast cell activity. You also will read about the important role that yeast plays in our daily lives.

OBJECTIVES FOR THIS LESSON

Observe evidence of yeast activity.

Design and conduct an inquiry to investigate substances that will or will not promote yeast activity.

Explain how different kinds of yeasts benefit or harm humans.

Update the yeast organism photo card.

INTRODUCING YEAST

There are many species of yeasts. They are divided among three different phyla of the Fungi kingdom. Most yeast species, however, belong to
the phylum Ascomycetes. In addition to yeasts, this phylum includes
truffles, morels, and mildew. Most fungi are multicellular and relatively
large. Yeast cells are unusual because they are unicellular and microscopic. Scientists believe that yeast once had the typical fungi's ability
to form hyphae—the tubes that root fungi to the surface of an object—
but gradually lost that ability.

Dry granules of yeast contain tiny spore sacs. In a moist, warm environment in which a food source is available, the spores become active;
during this period they grow into new yeast organisms and begin to
reproduce. Although yeast cells can reproduce sexually, they usually
reproduce asexually through a form of cell division called "budding." In
this process, a new cell forms by cell division and produces a small outgrowth on an older cell. Eventually, the smaller cell breaks off and
becomes self-sufficient.

(continued)

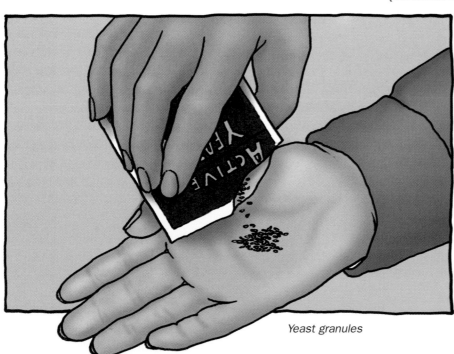

Yeast granules

(continued)

When yeast cells become active and feed, they undergo a process called "fermentation." During this process, sugar is broken down and carbon dioxide and alcohol are formed. In this lesson, you will see and measure evidence of yeast activity as yeast grains are added to different substances.

Nineteenth-century microbiologist Louis Pasteur first cultivated yeast cells and used them for scientific purposes.

MATERIALS FOR LESSON 15

For your group

1 copy of Student Sheet 15.1: Investigating the Effect of Two Substances on Yeast Activity

1 set of organism photo cards

2 metric rulers, 30 cm (12 in.)

3 test tubes, 25 mm × 150 mm

1 test tube rack

1 10-mL graduated cylinder

1 250-mL beaker

1 black marker

3 stirrers

Getting Started

1. With the class, read "Introducing Yeast" at the beginning of this lesson. Then observe and participate as your teacher provides more information about yeast.

2. In your science notebook, divide the list of substances your teacher shows you into two groups. In the first group, include the substances that you predict will promote yeast activity. In the second group, include those substances that you predict will not promote yeast activity.

3. Share your lists with the class.

Inquiry 15.1
Exploring Yeast Cell Activity

PROCEDURE

1. Choose one substance from each of the groups you made during "Getting Started."

2. Work with your group to devise and outline an inquiry on Student Sheet 15.1: Investigating the Effect of Two Substances on Yeast Activity to investigate whether the two substances you selected were placed in the correct group. For Step B (What I think will happen and why), write one sentence about each of the two substances, telling why you placed each in its group and what you think will happen when they are mixed with yeast cells. Be sure to include a valid control and an explanation of when and how you will measure your results. Your outline should include items A–F in the list that follows. Your final inquiry should include items A–H, which can also be found on your student sheet.

   A. Question I will try to answer

   B. What I think will happen and why

   C. Materials I will use

   D. At least four things I will keep the same (you may list more)

   E. Procedure I will follow

   F. Data table

   G. Graph of my findings

   H. What I found out

3. After you complete your inquiry design, read "Yeast: Rising to the Occasion" at the end of this lesson. You will conduct your inquiry, beginning with Procedure Step 4, during the next class period.

4. If necessary, work with your group to finish outlining your inquiry.

5. Use the black marker to label each of your three test tubes with the name of the substance you are testing.

6. Conduct the inquiry that you designed during class period 1.

7. At the appropriate time, complete and record any necessary measurements. Exchange information with other groups until you have data for all of the substances. If other groups tested the same substances as your group did, average their data with yours and record only the average.

8. Follow your teacher's directions for cleaning up and returning your materials.

9. Graph your findings and complete step H on your student sheet.

10. Update your group's organism photo card for yeast.

REFLECTING ON WHAT YOU'VE DONE

1. Answer the following questions on Student Sheet 15.1 and discuss your responses with the class:

A. If the foam column for either of the mixtures you tested was not as high as the column produced in the sugar solution, would you classify that substance as a promoter or non-promoter of yeast activity? Explain.

B. Were the predictions you made in "Getting Started" correct? Explain.

C. Were your results consistent with those of other students who tested the same substances? If not, explain why you think they differed.

D. Did any of your results surprise you? If so, which results and why?

2. Refer to "Yeast: Rising to the Occasion" at the end of this lesson to respond to the following on Student Sheet 15.1:

E. Explain one way in which yeast can be harmful to humans.

F. Explain two ways in which we use yeast to our advantage.

3. Visit the STC/MS™ Web site (http://www.stcms.si.edu) to find out more about yeast.

Yeast: Rising to the Occasion

Yeast cells sure do get around. You'd be surprised at all the places you can find them. These tiny, one-celled organisms live all around us—in soil and saltwater, on plant leaves and flowers. Neither plants nor animals, yeast cells are fungi.

Like other fungi, yeast cells are very good at recycling. They stay busy by decomposing, or breaking down, plant and animal matter. As they do this, they grow and reproduce, and in the process, carbon dioxide and alcohol are released. For this reason, yeast cells play an important role in some basic food processes, such as making bread dough rise and fermenting substances to produce wine, beer, and industrial alcohol.

The Yeast Within

Yeast cells not only live all around us, they also live upon us and within us! The oily surfaces of our noses, ears, and scalps are favorite hangouts. And so are our mouths and intestinal tracts. It may seem weird, but it's all perfectly normal.

Most of the time, the yeast populations on our bodies are present in numbers that cause no problems. Sometimes, such as when we take certain medications or change our diets, yeast colonies are able to multiply rapidly. This can lead to infections. Too many yeast cells in the lining of our mouths, for example, can cause thrush, a contagious disease found most often among babies and children. Symptoms of thrush include fever and diarrhea, and small whitish bumps on the mouth, throat, and tongue.

Fermentation

Most of us know yeast best from its role in breadmaking. When the conditions are right, yeast cells make the bread dough rise, or expand. They do so during a chemical process called "fermentation." Fermentation is the process through which cells get energy by breaking down simple sugars without using oxygen. Many kinds of yeast cells can ferment sugars, and different yeast cells accomplish this in slightly different ways. Brewer's yeast and baker's yeast are important to the food industry because they break down sugars into carbon dioxide and alcohol.

Here's how it works during breadmaking. Baker's yeast, which looks like little dry granules, actually consists of tiny sacs that are full of spores. When mixed with water and added to

Yeast budding

T.K. MAUGEL, LABORATORY FOR BIOLOGICAL ULTRASTRUCTURE, UNIVERSITY OF MARYLAND, COLLEGE PARK

The dough used to make the bread in the upper photo had no yeast added. Yeast was added to the dough for the bread in the lower photo.

the warm, moist dough, the yeast cells become active. They begin to reproduce by budding and form new yeast organisms. The small buds break off, forming smaller cells from larger ones.

During this activity, fermentation occurs, releasing carbon dioxide and alcohol. The gas becomes trapped in the sticky dough and can't immediately escape—so it makes the bread dough expand. When you look closely at a piece of bread, you can often see little holes where the carbon dioxide bubbles have been. When the bread is baked, the dough stays in this expanded shape. The heat from the oven causes the alcohol to evaporate. It also kills the yeast organisms.

Brewer's yeast is used to make beer or wine. The bubbles in certain wines, such as champagne, come from carbon dioxide that gets released when grape juice ferments.

Get Around

Breaking down plant and animal matter in our soil and water. Guarding our bodies against harmful microorganisms. Making our wines bubble and our breads rise. Causing illnesses and rashes. There's no doubt about it—yeast cells are extremely busy, often useful, and occasionally irritating, organisms. ☐

Yeast has been important to wine production for a long time. Before 2000 B.C., the Egyptians knew if they crushed grapes, alcohol would be produced.

16

Introducing *Daphnia*

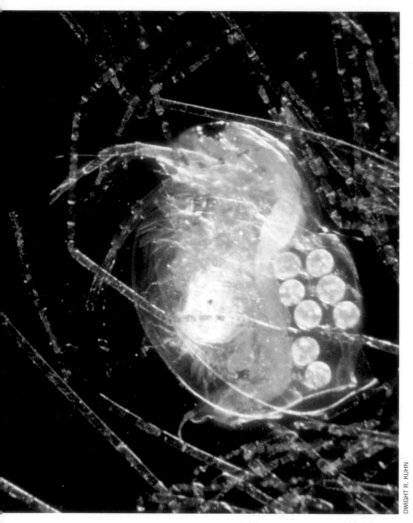

Daphnia's *transparent outer shell makes it easy to observe its internal structures.*

INTRODUCTION

In this lesson, you will explore some features and behaviors of an organism called *Daphnia*. You will observe the organism through a microscope and prepare a scientific drawing of a *Daphnia* and some of its structures. Finally, you will measure a *Daphnia*'s heart rate before and after the organism has been treated with two different chemicals.

OBJECTIVES FOR THIS LESSON

Observe, sketch, and measure a *Daphnia* and identify its major structures.

Determine the heart rate of a *Daphnia* under various conditions.

Update your organism photo card for *Daphnia.*

Getting Started

1. *Daphnia* are related to lobsters and shrimp. List in your science notebook some of the characteristics you think these three organisms share. Use Figures 16.1 and 16.2 and the Introduction photo on the first page of this lesson for reference.

2. Answer the following questions in your science notebook and share your responses with the class.

A. What kind of skeleton do *Daphnia*, lobsters, and shrimp have?

B. What are the advantages and disadvantages of this kind of skeleton over the type of skeletons humans have?

MATERIALS FOR LESSON 16

For you

1 copy of Student Sheet 16.1: Template for *Daphnia* Drawing

1 copy of Student Sheet 16.2A: Table for Recording Heartbeats of *Daphnia*

1 copy of Student Sheet 16.2B: Effect of Alcohol and Cola Solutions on the Heart Rate of *Daphnia*

For your group

1 set of organism photo cards

2 compound light microscopes

2 depression slides

2 strands of cotton

2 coverslips

4 *Daphnia* (2 per class period)

2 metric rulers, 30 cm (12 in.)

2 transparent rulers

4 black markers with ultrafine points

Figure 16.2 *Shrimp*

Figure 16.1 *Spiny lobster*

Inquiry 16.1
Preparing a Scientific Drawing of a *Daphnia*

PROCEDURE

1. You will work in pairs for this inquiry. Have one student from your pair go to the materials station to obtain a slide with a *Daphnia* in a drop or two of spring water. One or two strands of cotton will isolate the *Daphnia* in a small area for viewing. Do not press down on the coverslip.

2. Use your microscope to focus on the *Daphnia* under the highest power at which you can see the entire organism.

3. Draw the *Daphnia* in as much detail as you can on Student Sheet 16.1. Follow the guidelines for scientific drawings listed on Student Sheet 2.3A. Title your drawing "*Daphnia*: The Water Flea." Refer to "The Transparent Water Flea" at the end of this lesson for information about how to label your drawing.

4. Use your transparent ruler to measure the length of the *Daphnia*. Record the length, following the guidelines for scientific drawings.

5. Take the following steps to observe and identify specific structures to include in your drawing. (Refer to Figure 16.3 and the illustration and photo in "The Transparent Water Flea.")

A. Look for the intestine, which runs from the mouth to the anus. Notice its color. Discuss with your partner why you think it is this color.

B. Locate the *Daphnia*'s heart. Notice how rapidly it beats.

C. Find the "brood chamber," a sac located just below the heart of the female *Daphnia*. Discuss with your partner what might be found inside a brood chamber.

D. Focus on your *Daphnia*'s eye. Switch the microscope to a higher power to observe the eye in greater detail. Discuss with your partner how its structure differs from that of a human eye.

E. Focus on one of the antennae under high power. Discuss with your partner one possible function of the antennae.

F. Focus on one of the legs under high power. Notice the bristles. Discuss with your partner what you think the function of the bristles may be.

6. When you and your partner have completed your drawings, move to Inquiry 16.2 if instructed to do so by your teacher. Use the same slide but get a fresh *Daphnia* for this inquiry if you will be completing the inquiry during the same period. Follow your teacher's instructions for returning the *Daphnia* to the culture container.

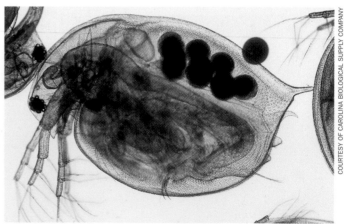

Figure 16.3 *You can easily see the digestive tube, heart, and brood chamber in the* Daphnia *at the center of this photo.*

COURTESY OF CAROLINA BIOLOGICAL SUPPLY COMPANY

Inquiry 16.2
Exploring the Effect of Alcohol and Cola Solutions on the Heart Rate of *Daphnia*

PROCEDURE

1. Read all of the Procedure Steps carefully. They will give you the information necessary to prepare a data table in the box provided on Student Sheet 16.2B. You will record your data and your partner's data on this table.

2. Observe the *Daphnia* closely. Practice measuring its heartbeat using the following technique:

A. Place a pencil or fine line marker in your writing hand and hold the tip just above the middle of the top left box on Student Sheet 16.2A.

B. For 10 seconds, tap the point of your pencil in the first box, making a mark each time the *Daphnia*'s heart beats. Have your partner time you and call "Stop" when 10 seconds are up. If you need more practice, make your marks in the right box in the top row.

3. When you have finished practicing, move your pencil so that you are holding the tip above the middle of the first box in the second row. Have your partner time you for 10 seconds while you mark each heart beat.

4. Count the number of marks to determine the number of times your *Daphnia*'s heart beats in 10 seconds. Decide with your partner how to use this figure to calculate the *Daphnia*'s heart rate per minute. Record this calculation in the appropriate place on your data table.

5. Repeat Step 4, using a different box for your marks. Use your data from the two

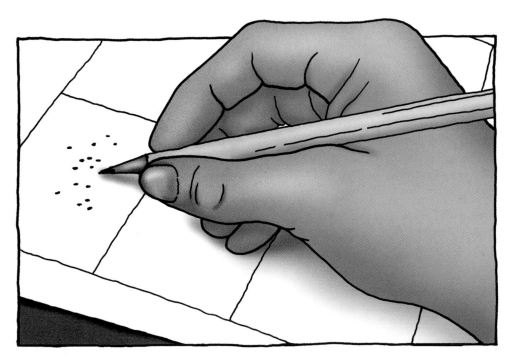

Figure 16.4 *Each dot represents one beat of the* Daphnia *'s heart.*

trials to calculate the average heart rate of the *Daphnia* in spring water.

6. Switch roles with your partner and repeat Steps 2–5.

7. You have measured and recorded your *Daphnia*'s average heart rate while it was in a drop of spring water. Now, one pair in your group will measure a *Daphnia*'s heart rate while the organism is immersed in a weak alcohol solution. The other pair will do the same while its *Daphnia* is immersed in a weak cola solution. Before you begin, write one-sentence answers to the following questions on Student Sheet 16.2B:

A. How do you think alcohol will affect the heart rate of *Daphnia*? Why?

B. How do you think cola will affect the heart rate of *Daphnia*? Why?

8. Watch and listen as your teacher demonstrates how to add the alcohol and cola solutions to the *Daphnia* slides.

9. Have one pair in your group add a drop of weak alcohol solution to its *Daphnia* in the manner demonstrated by your teacher. Have the other pair in your group add a drop of weak cola solution to its *Daphnia*. Let the slides sit for about 2 minutes.

10. Have one partner of each pair record the *Daphnia*'s heartbeats in a box on Student Sheet 16.2A, while the other partner keeps time for 10 seconds.

11. Switch roles and repeat Step 10. Calculate the average heartbeat per minute for the two trials and record it on the data table.

12. Exchange information with your group members.

13. Follow your teacher's directions for returning the *Daphnia* to its container.

REFLECTING ON WHAT YOU'VE DONE

1. On the basis of what you have learned in this lesson, answer the following questions on Student Sheet 16.2B:

A. What effect does cola have on the heart rate of *Daphnia*? Explain.

B. What effect does alcohol have on the heart rate of *Daphnia*? Explain.

C. How would you expect your heart rate to change if you drank a large quantity of cola or alcohol?

2. Refer to the reading selection "The Transparent Water Flea" to respond to the following on Student Sheet 16.2B:

D. List three ways in which *Daphnia* are similar to other crustaceans.

E. Explain why *Daphnia* are referred to as "water fleas."

F. Explain one function of the bristles on a *Daphnia*'s legs.

3. Revise as necessary the responses you made during "Getting Started." Discuss your changes with the class.

The *Transparent* Water Flea

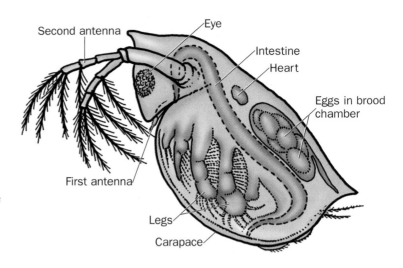

Like the cabbage white butterfly and the WOWBug, *Daphnia* belong to the phylum of jointed-limbed organisms called Arthropods. Like shrimp, crabs, and lobsters, *Daphnia* are members of a class of Arthropods called crustaceans. Crustaceans are characterized by an external skeleton, gills for gas exchange, two pairs of antennae, and numerous jointed appendages. Different species of *Daphnia* range in length from around 0.2 millimeters to more than 5 millimeters.

Daphnia are particularly interesting animals to study because their exoskeletons, or carapaces, are transparent. This makes it easy to observe and identify their internal organs with a hand lens or a microscope. Their hearts beat very rapidly, pumping blood throughout their bodies. Their intestine, tubular in shape, extends from mouth to anus. Female *Daphnia* have a large brood chamber just below their heart. The brood chamber holds the female's eggs.

Daphnia have been called "water fleas" because they move with a jerky motion that resembles the way a flea jumps. They do this by quickly flipping their antennae downward. They control their depth in the water by adjusting the movement of their antennae like a parachute.

Daphnia can survive in almost any freshwater environment—lakes, ponds, streams, swamps, and marshes. They feed on microscopic organisms such as bacteria, algae, and protozoa. *Daphnia* propel food toward their mouths using water currents that they generate with their leg movements. They filter out food particles with the bristles on their legs. Then they pass the food from the bristles to their mouths.

In their lifetime, female *Daphnia* produce up to 400 eggs. Reproduction in *Daphnia* is unusual because the eggs develop in the female's brood chamber without being fertilized. Offspring are fully developed when they hatch.

Because *Daphnia* reproduce so rapidly, they are an important source of food for many other organisms, especially fish. They provide an important link in the food chain between the microscopic organisms upon which they prey and the larger organisms that prey upon them. ☐

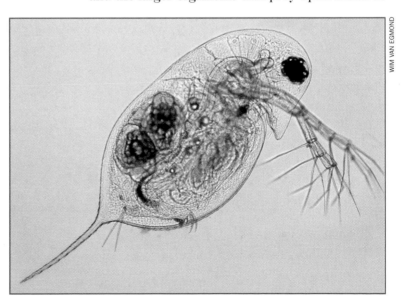

This Daphnia *has just eaten some algae. How can you tell?*

LESSON 17
Exploring the *Hydra*

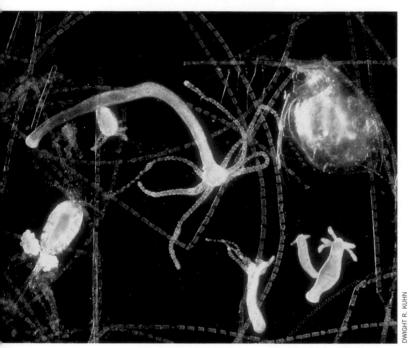

A great variety of organisms, including Hydra, may be found in a small quantity of pond water.

INTRODUCTION

When you hear the word "*Hydra*," you may think of the nine-headed mythological beast with poisonous breath slain by Hercules. When you observe a multicellular *Hydra* under the microscope, you'll better understand how it got its name. The *Hydra* is a relative of the more familiar, and often feared, jellyfish. In this lesson, you will observe, sketch, and measure a *Hydra*. You also will observe the way it obtains its food, reacts to touch, and reproduces asexually.

OBJECTIVES FOR THIS LESSON

Observe, sketch, and measure a *Hydra* and label its prominent features.

Observe a *Hydra*'s methods of obtaining food and reacting to touch.

Observe a *Hydra*'s method of asexual reproduction.

Update the organism photo card for *Hydra*.

Based on this illustration, how do you think the *Hydra* got its name? Which of these dictionary definitions applies to the *Hydra* in this lesson?

1: a nine-headed serpent or monster of Greek mythology slain by Hercules, each head of which when cut off is replaced by two others

2: a multifarious evil not to be overcome by a single effort

3: a southern constellation of great length that lies south of Cancer, Sextans, Corvus, and Virgo and is represented on old maps by a serpent

4: any of numerous small tubular freshwater hydrozoans (as of the genus *Hydra*)

Getting Started

1. Have one student from each pair take the depression slide to your teacher to obtain a *Hydra*.

2. At your seat, take turns observing the *Hydra* under 40×. Then respond to the following in your science notebook:

A. *Describe the* Hydra *in one or two sentences.*

B. *List any organisms you think are similar to the* Hydra.

C. *How do you think the* Hydra *obtains its food?*

3. Discuss your observations and responses with the class.

MATERIALS FOR LESSON 17

For you
1 copy of Student Sheet 17.1: Template for *Hydra* Drawing
1 copy of Student Sheet 17.3: Template for *Hydra* Budding Drawing

For your group
1 set of organism photo cards
2 *Hydra*
1 prepared slide of *Hydra* budding
1 blackworm fragment
1 *Daphnia*
2 compound light microscopes
2 plastic slides
2 coverslips
2 dissecting needles
2 metric rulers, 30 cm (12 in.)
2 transparent rulers
1 black marker

Inquiry 17.1
Observing and Sketching a *Hydra*

PROCEDURE

1. Focus on a *Hydra* under 40×. Slowly move the slide so you can see the entire organism.

2. In the upper circle on Student Sheet 17.1: Template for *Hydra* Drawing, draw the entire *Hydra* in detail. Refer to "The *Hydra*: Up Close and Personal" at the end of this lesson for labeling information.

3. Place the transparent ruler underneath the slide. Position the ruler so that you can measure the *Hydra*'s length. Record it in the appropriate place on your drawing.

4. While looking through the microscope, gently touch a tentacle with the tip of a dissecting needle. Discuss with your partner the reaction of the *Hydra* to your touch. Discuss the *Hydra*'s reaction speed compared to how fast you would react if you were touched with the point of a pin.

5. Move on to Inquiry 17.2, using the same *Hydra* and slide.

Inquiry 17.2
Feeding the *Hydra*

PROCEDURE

1. One student from each pair should bring the *Hydra* slide to the materials station to obtain either a *Daphnia* or a blackworm fragment from your teacher.

2. Focus on the *Hydra* under 40×. If you have a *Daphnia,* keep watching until it brushes against the tentacles of the *Hydra*. If you have a blackworm, use the tip of your dissecting needle to nudge it toward the *Hydra*. Refer to the reading selections at the end of this lesson if necessary to respond to the following questions on Student Sheet 17.1:

A. How does the *Hydra* behave when the *Daphnia* or blackworm touches its tentacles?

B. How do you think the *Hydra* is able to trap organisms that are so much larger than it is?

C. How does the *Hydra* take the organism into its body?

3. Follow your teacher's directions for returning the organisms.

are produced are able to survive the colder conditions, while the parents cannot.

The *Hydra* has no circulatory system with a heart and blood vessels. Because its body is only two cell-layers thick, the *Hydra*'s cells can get the nutrients it needs through a process called "diffusion." This occurs as the *Hydra* moves through the water and the cells interact with the environment, exchanging oxygen and food for carbon dioxide and other wastes through the cell membranes.

The *Hydra*'s outer layer of cells protects the organism. Its inner layer of cells secretes enzymes that digest the *Hydra*'s food.

The *Hydra* does not have a central nervous system. Instead, it has a "nerve net" through which impulses that control the *Hydra*'s muscle contractions are carried. These contractions allow the *Hydra* to expand, contract, and move about.

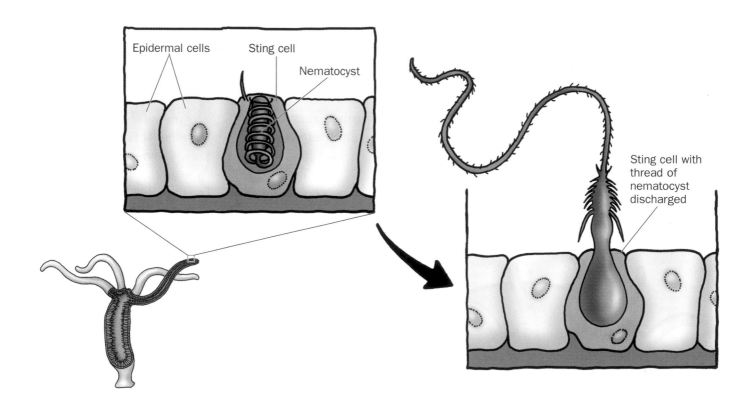

Notice the coiled thread inside the sting cell on the left. It has been discharged from the sting cell on the right.

Paralyzing Poisons and Tight Embraces

The *Hydra* feeds on small organisms, such as *Daphnia*. Specialized cells that make up part of the outer layer of a *Hydra* contain stinging structures called "nematocysts." When an organism such as *Daphnia* brushes against the *Hydra*'s tentacles, the nematocysts shoot out threads. These threads pierce the prey and release a paralyzing poison. Other nematocysts release threads that surround the prey and hold it tight. The tentacles then move the prey toward the *Hydra*'s mouth and force it into its digestive cavity.

The *Hydra* secretes digestive enzymes into this cavity from cells in the inner layer. These enzymes break down the prey into usable nutrients. Whip-like flagella, which line the digestive cavity, wave about to stir the digestive fluid. Undigested pieces are released through the *Hydra*'s mouth. Digested nutrients move into the cells of the *Hydra* by diffusion.

The *Hydra* spends much of its time attached to a surface by its base. However, when it's time to move, the *Hydra* moves in style. It simply floats or travels from one location to another by doing somersaults! □

COURTESY OF CAROLINA BIOLOGICAL SUPPLY COMPANY

This Hydra *has captured and paralyzed a minnow. Is it biting off more than it can chew?*

The Hydra *is somewhat of a gymnast, often performing somersaults to move from one place to another.*

Jellyfish Get a Bad Rap

Consider jellyfish. They may look like jelly, but they're not really fish at all. In fact, they are close relatives of *Hydra*. Their reputation for stinging has made them very unpopular. And it's really not fair. They're poor swimmers and often bump into things—including people. When jellyfish sense movement nearby, barbed, threadlike stingers automatically shoot out from their tentacles. It's a good strategy for stunning and killing small fish and other prey—but not the best for making friends.

Luckily, most people who get stung by jellyfish only develop a red, itchy rash that goes away in a few hours. Putting ice on a sting often makes it feel better. That is, unless you get stung by a Portuguese man-of-war, a type of jellyfish found in warm seas. Then, look out for painful welts and a fever—and maybe a trip to the hospital.

The Portuguese man-of-war, while impressive, is perhaps not the most dangerous jellyfish. In the warm waters of the Great Barrier Reef of Australia, a relatively small species, the box jellyfish, terrorizes swimmers. Its poison is extremely potent and life-threatening. At some popular beaches, jellyfish nets are installed around the perimeter of swimming areas to protect people from encounters with these organisms.

As for jellyfish you may find lifeless on the beach—beware! Stingers can shoot out for a few hours even after a jellyfish has died.

Mostly Water

Jellyfish are invertebrates, which means they have no backbone. But that's not the half of it.

Box jellyfish

COURTESY "ALL STINGS CONSIDERED" BY CRAIG THOMAS, M.D., AND SUSAN SCOTT

Jellyfish also have no brain, heart, blood, bones, eyes, ears, or gills. In fact, they're 95 percent water! Most are bell-shaped, and through their hollow transparent bodies you can see—if you care to—what they had for lunch.

Jellyfish can alternately contract and relax their bell-shaped bodies to push themselves along in the water. But much of the time they simply drift along on ocean currents, with their tentacles—which can range in length from only 1 centimeter to as much as 30 meters—trailing below them.

Considering how old they are, jellyfish get very little respect. These ocean dwellers have been floating around since long before the dinosaurs! And it's not as if they have it easy. Many kinds of fish, as well as sea turtles and marine birds, seek them out for food.

Numbers Out of Whack

These days, jellyfish are becoming even more disliked because in some areas, they have become so numerous and eat so much that fish, shrimp, crab, and other seafood are in short supply. This threatens the livelihood of people living around the Gulf of Mexico and elsewhere who make their living by fishing.

But again, you can't blame jellyfish. Their numbers increase when oxygen levels in the water are low, something that happens when a lot of fertilizer and waste products get dumped into the water. In addition, in some areas overfishing has left jellyfish with few predators. ◻

Jellyfish are left behind when the tide goes out in Cottonwood Bay, Alaska. They may still sting for a short time after they die.

18
The Next Generation: Part 1

In nature, some plants, like this dandelion, have unique ways of dispersing their seeds.

DWIGHT R. KUHN

INTRODUCTION

It has been about 20 days since you last pollinated your Fast Plants flowers. The seed pods have dried and the enclosed seeds have turned brown as they matured. In this lesson, you will harvest your seeds and prepare them for germination in a manner that allows you to observe certain inherited traits in the sprouts. (In Lesson 19, you will observe one of your sprouts' traits that will give clues to the genetic makeup of its parents.) You complete this lesson by reading about grafting, and about the cabbage white butterfly and how its life cycle interacts with those of plants from the cabbage family.

OBJECTIVES FOR THIS LESSON

Recognize the pod as a fruit and the fruit as a package for seeds.

Develop a list of ways in which seeds are dispersed.

Harvest the F_2-generation Wisconsin Fast Plants seeds, set them up for germination, and predict the number of purple-pigmented offspring.

Review the relationship between the life cycles of Wisconsin Fast Plants and cabbage white butterflies.

Getting Started

MATERIALS FOR LESSON 18

For you

1 copy of Student
   Sheet 18.1:
   Wisconsin Fast
   Plants Seed Data

For your group

1 set of organism
  photo cards
1 Fast Plants growing
  system
1 plastic cup, 24 oz
1 petri dish with lid
1 pair of forceps
1 pair of scissors
2 paper towels
1 black marker

1. Look at the photo at the beginning of this lesson. The dandelion has a unique way of making sure its seeds get dispersed, or transported, to other places. Work with your group to list four ways in which seeds may be dispersed by plants.

2. Discuss your list with the class.

Coconut palms have an interesting method of dispersing their seeds. The palm's fruit consists of a fibrous husk that encloses a large seed. The husk has enough air inside to allow it to float. Sitting high in the water, the husk acts as a sailboat, moving long distances with the wind's assistance! This coconut has washed up on a sandy shore and germinated. Because of the coconut's ability to float, almost all of the Pacific islands are populated by coconut trees.

7. Position the plastic cup containing the petri dish in the plant light house so that the light is about 5 cm from the seeds.

8. Place the remaining seeds into a container provided by your teacher.

9. Update your group's organism photo card for Wisconsin Fast Plants.

REFLECTING ON WHAT YOU'VE DONE

On the basis of what you learned in this lesson, respond to the following on Student Sheet 18.1:

A. What initiated the formation of the seed pods?

B. What do you think determines the number of seeds found in each pod?

C. Was it more than mere luck that the seeds came out of the pods so easily? Explain.

D. In Lesson 9, you counted the number of Fast Plants that displayed a purple pigment in their stem and leaves. You recorded this number in your science notebook. You pollinated these plants and harvested their seeds. You chose 36 of these seeds and set them up for germination in your group's petri dish. If all of the seeds germinated, how many of the sprouts do you predict will display the purple pigment? Explain your answer.

E. Luther Burbank, a California plant breeder, grafted branches from many kinds of fruit—pears, plums, peaches, and different varieties of apples—onto one apple tree. If seeds produced by one of the apple blossoms germinated and grew into a tree, how many kinds of fruit would you expect to find on the new tree and why?

F. What would happen to cabbage white butterflies if all the plants in the mustard family on Earth died? Explain your answer.

G. Why do you think some species of plants produce only one seed in a fruit, while others produce thousands of seeds?

H. Of what importance to the plant is the dispersal of seeds?

GROWING SEEDLESS FRUITS

You are at a summer picnic at a friend's house. You bite into a juicy slice of watermelon. But what do you do with the seeds? Should you spit them on the ground or perhaps into a napkin?

Well, your seed-spitting days may be over. That's because now you can buy seedless watermelons. In fact, there are many kinds of seedless fruits, including grapes and oranges. But if there are no seeds, how do people grow more seedless fruits?

Two Plants Make One

If you've ever had a garden, you know how to plant seeds in soil to create new plants. But fruit plants are not always grown from seeds. A process called "grafting," a method of joining two plants together, is used to produce most fruit plants, including some seedless ones.

The lower part of a graft is called the "understock." After grafting is completed, the understock is referred to as the "rootstock." It provides a root system for the new plant. The upper part of a graft is called a "scion." It normally consists of a part of the plant's previous year's growth, along with one or more buds. Eventually, the rootstock and scion fuse to form a single plant.

One of the main reasons for grafting is to improve the quantity and/or quality of a plant. For example, a graft may combine a quality rootstock (one that is resistant to fungal disease, insect attack, or drought, or that grows best in certain soil conditions) with a scion with superior fruit quality (higher sweetness, larger size, longer shelf life). Or the rootstock may be combined with a scion that will bear a greater quantity of fruit.

In order to grow more seedless fruit, a scion from an existing seedless fruit plant is attached to the understock of a seed-producing plant of the same kind. For example, a bud from a seedless orange tree can be grafted to the understock of another orange tree. The bud and roots join, and a new tree eventually grows.

In the late 1800s, the French wine industry was in danger of ruin by an insect-transmitted disease. An entomologist, Charles V. Riley, took a native American grape rootstock to France. The French grape vines were grafted to the American rootstock, which was resistant to the disease. The process of grafting produced a disease-resistant grape plant that still thrives today. Mr. Riley received high praise from the French government for saving the country's wine industry because, at that time, grafting was a novel idea. The government even gave Mrs. Riley a diamond necklace in appreciation for her husband's work!

Grafters use a 2.5-centimeter-wide tape to secure the graft. The tape will remain until it breaks down from weathering.

The Cabbage White Butterfly

Chances are you've seen cabbage white butterflies flitting about in your neighborhood. They are one of the most common butterfly species in the world. From city gardens to country fields, from coasts to deserts, cabbage whites are found nearly everywhere.

Like all butterflies, the cabbage white goes through metamorphosis. It starts out as an egg, completes five larval stages, becomes a chrysalis, and emerges as a butterfly. As a larva, it feeds on a number of plants of the mustard family, including cabbage, cauliflower, radish, Wisconsin Fast Plants, and many other cultivated and wild species.

From Egg to Caterpillar

Deposited on the underside of a leaf of a host plant, such as a Wisconsin Fast Plant, the creamy yellow egg of a cabbage white butterfly begins to develop. After 2 to 4 days, a larva chews its way through the top of the egg. Like the head of a human baby, a newly hatched larva's head is quite large compared with its body. The larva often eats its shell; it might even feed on some of the nearby eggs that have not hatched.

Cabbage whites have five larval stages, or instars. The first instar begins when the larva emerges from the egg. Each of the next four instars is defined by a new molt, or shedding of the skin. When ready to molt, the larva seeks a dry site and weaves a fine pad of silk from a silk gland located in its head. The larva clings to the pad with its legs and rests quietly. In a short while, its skin cracks, and a larger larva crawls out. A larva grows quickly, molting two or three times during its first week.

By the fourth and fifth instars, larvae have begun to feed voraciously and can be quite destructive. They devour their favorite plants, leaving only stems and large leaf veins. By now, the larvae are up to 3 centimeters long. They are bright green with pale yellow stripes running the length of their bodies on their back and sides. Their color provides a good camouflage. Because the larvae often feed on the upper surfaces of leaves in broad daylight, their color probably helps keep them from becoming a meal for a hungry bird.

(continued)

The leaf shows both eggs and newly hatched larvae, which have only just begun their feeding frenzy.

As you can see, this larva's color helps hide it from predators.

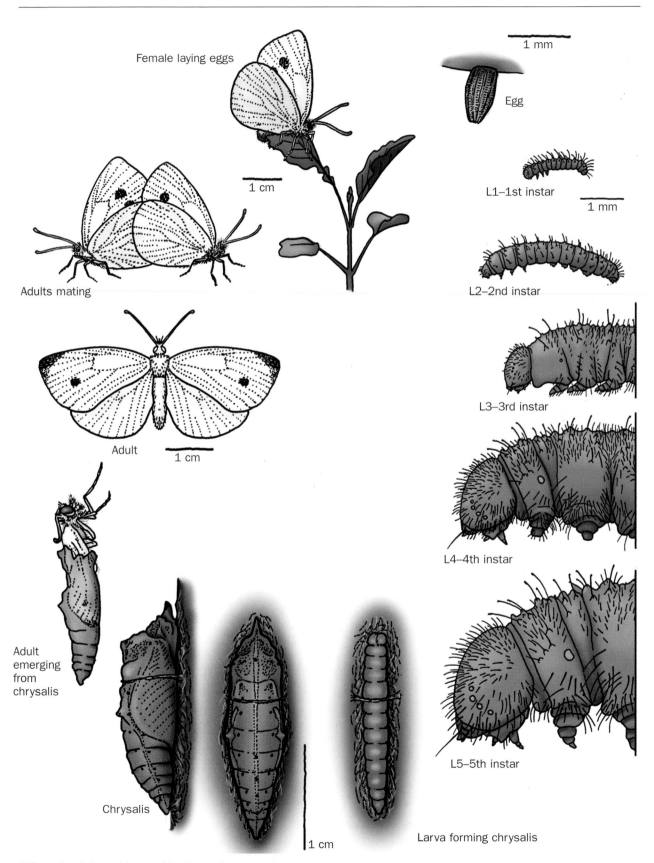

Female laying eggs

1 mm

Egg

1 cm

Adults mating

L1–1st instar

1 mm

L2–2nd instar

Adult

1 cm

L3–3rd instar

L4–4th instar

Adult emerging from chrysalis

Chrysalis

1 cm

L5–5th instar

Larva forming chrysalis

Life cycle of the cabbage white butterfly

From Chrysalis to Butterfly

By the time it has fed for 10 to 12 days, the fifth instar caterpillar is fully grown. At this time, it begins to search for a sheltered place to pupate, or form a chrysalis. At first, the chrysalis is green. But it can change color, depending on how much light it gets and on the color of the surface to which it is attached. For example, a chrysalis on a dark surface can turn dark brown. This color is produced by melanin, the same pigment that colors human skin and hair.

Inside the chrysalis, important changes take place. And because the chrysalis is somewhat transparent, it is easy to watch the development of various features of the butterfly. In about 2 to 3 days, the outlines of the wings appear. During the next 2 days, one or two dark spots appear in the center of the wings. Finally, a dark spot appears at the tip of the wings. The butterfly emerges about 24 hours after these spots appear.

Once it begins to emerge, the cabbage white butterfly takes less than a minute to get out of its chrysalis. The wobbly new butterfly walks to a high location, hangs quietly, and allows its wings to expand and harden. This process takes about 2 hours. And then it's off to find food.

COURTESY OF WISCONSIN FAST PLANTS

This is a top view of chrysalises from early to late stages of development. A butterfly soon will emerge from the chrysalis on the right.

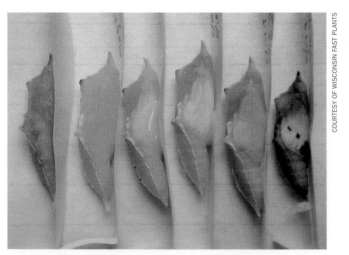

COURTESY OF WISCONSIN FAST PLANTS

This is a side view of six chrysalises from early to late stages of development.

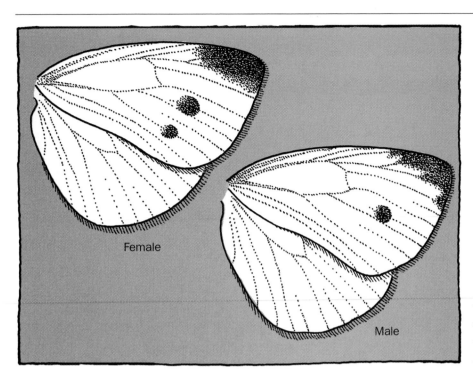

Female

Male

Male cabbage whites usually have one central black spot on their forewings; females have two.

Feeding, Mating, and Reproducing

The cabbage white butterfly feeds on sugar, water, minerals, and other nutrients from the nectar of various flowers. The butterfly's mouth, or proboscis, works like a straw. When the butterfly detects nectar, it uncoils its proboscis and sips it. When the butterfly finishes feeding, it rolls up its proboscis.

You might think the cabbage white butterfly, which feeds continuously, will grow big and fat. Actually, butterflies do not grow bigger, no matter how much food they consume. They use the sugar obtained from nectar as their energy source, much like we obtain quick energy from a candy bar.

The adult butterfly's life is devoted solely to reproduction. During the day, males search for females with which to mate. Females signal their readiness to mate by releasing a special odor, or pheromone, that is very attractive to searching males. After mating, females look for host plants on which to lay their eggs.

Cabbage whites, like most other butterflies, have a short life span. They live only about 3 weeks. During this time females lay up to 300 eggs, enough to provide for the survival to adulthood of a new generation. Over a summer, your garden may be home to two or three generations of cabbage whites. In the fall, as the daylight hours decrease, chrysalises enter a resting state, called "diapause," that permits them to withstand the harsh environment of winter. Warm spring temperatures stimulate the emergence of adults from the chrysalises, and the cycle of life continues. ☐

This is the normal mating position of cabbage whites. If disturbed during mating, they can maintain this position even during flight.

COURTESY OF WISCONSIN FAST PLANTS

19

The Next Generation: Part 2— Secrets Revealed

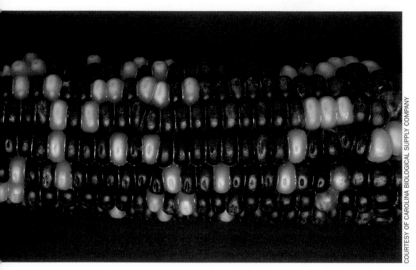

Each kernel on this ear of corn is a seed. The colors of the seeds obviously vary. Think about why as you conduct the inquiries in this lesson.

COURTESY OF CAROLINA BIOLOGICAL SUPPLY COMPANY

INTRODUCTION

By this time, your second generation of Wisconsin Fast Plants seeds should have germinated and the sprouts should be off to a good start. These sprouts offer clues about a specific inherited trait of Fast Plants. In this lesson, you will examine the sprouts and compare their features to those of their parents—the plants you cross pollinated in Lesson 9. You will learn about a very persistent monk who is called the "Father of Genetics," and you will likely make the same kind of intriguing discovery about heredity that he made. Next, you will simulate the processes of meiosis and fertilization to help you understand how different combinations of genes are passed from parents to offspring. You will apply your understanding of

OBJECTIVES FOR THIS LESSON

Observe your Wisconsin Fast Plants sprouts for clues about an inherited trait.

Demonstrate how certain genes interact in pairs to express dominant or recessive traits.

Discover by experimentation how Gregor Mendel established the fundamentals of heredity.

Observe evidence of the advantage of using large sample sizes when conducting an inquiry.

Identify homozygous and heterozygous gene pairs.

Participate in a simulation of meiosis and fertilization.

Demonstrate an understanding of the difference between genotype and phenotype.

Use a Punnett square to show how genes may pair during a genetic cross.

Create a cartoon character with specific traits determined by random pairings of genes.

Create a cartoon offspring based on the genotypes of its parents.

genetic pairings by creating a cartoon character with certain traits, pairing genes from your character with those from another to produce an offspring, and comparing and contrasting the offspring's traits with those of its parents.

Getting Started

1. Observe the parents and offspring in Figures 19.1 and 19.2. What clues about heredity do these photos offer? Discuss this with your group and list at least three of your ideas in your science notebook.

2. Discuss your observations with the class.

MATERIALS

For each student

- 1 copy of Student Sheet 19.1: Stem and Leaf Color in Wisconsin Fast Plants

For your group

- 1 petri dish with sprouts (prepared in Lesson 18)
- 1 copy of Student Sheet 19.2A: Traits, Meiosis, and Fertilization— Male
- 1 copy of Student Sheet 19.2B: Traits, Meiosis, and Fertilization— Female
- 2 copies of Student Sheet 19.3A: Introducing Clyde and Claire—Facial Traits
- 2 copies of Student Sheet 19.3B: Introducing Clyde and Claire— Determining Offspring Traits
- 2 copies of Student Sheet 19.3C: Introducing Clyde and Claire— Cartoon Facial Traits
- 2 pairs of scissors
- 6 sheets of copy paper
- 4 pieces of taster paper
- 4 pieces of control paper
- 4 black markers with ultrafine points
- 4 boxes of colored pencils Transparent tape
- 4 calculators
- 2 spinners

Figure 19.1

Figure 19.2

Inquiry 19.1
Observing the New Sprouts

PROCEDURE

1. Observe closely the plant in Figure 19.3. It is similar genetically and in appearance to both of the parents of your sprouts.

2. Now observe the sprouts in your petri dish. Count the number of sprouts with purple pigment and record that number on Student Sheet 19.1. Count the green sprouts (the ones with no sign of purple pigment at all) and record that number. Use a calculator to determine the ratio of purple to green sprouts.

3. Where do you think the green-pigmented Fast Plants came from when both parents displayed a purple pigment? To find out, read "Mendel's Discoveries." When directed, add data from other groups and classes to your student sheet. Working with the combined class data, use your calculator to determine the overall ratio of purple to green sprouts.

COURTESY OF CAROLINA BIOLOGICAL SUPPLY COMPANY

Figure 19.3 *The purple pigment in this plant is very obvious. Placing a Fast Plant with one or more genes for purple pigment close to the light source during development stimulates the production of the purple pigment.*

Inquiry 19.2
Making It More Personal

PROCEDURE

1. With the class, read "What Are the Chances?" which explains how genes pair randomly during meiosis and fertilization. Ask questions about anything you do not understand about this selection and about "Heredity—Passing It On," which you read for homework.

2. Working with a partner, try to position your tongue in the manner illustrated in Figure 19.4. If you can easily do so, you are a "tongue-roller." The tongue-roller gene (R) is dominant over the non-tongue-roller gene (r).

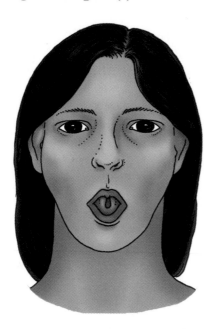

Figure 19.4 *If you can roll your tongue in this manner, you are carrying at least one dominant gene for tongue rolling.*

3. For this inquiry, record information about genetic traits of males on Student Sheet 19.2A and females on Student Sheet 19.2B. Look at the illustration of a chromosome on the top right portion of the appropriate student sheet. Record in the top gene location the symbols for the genes that reflect whether you are a tongue-roller or a non-tongue-roller. (During this inquiry, if you find that you have a given trait, assume that you are heterozygous for that trait, with one dominant and one recessive gene. For example, if you are a tongue-roller, assume that your gene pair is "Rr," as shown in Figure 19.5. If you are a non-tongue-roller, assume your gene pair is "rr.")

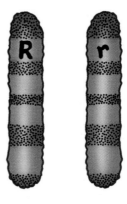

Figure 19.5 *If you have the tongue-roller trait, you are said to be "expressing" the gene for that trait. This is how the chromosomes will appear after you fill in the appropriate symbols for the tongue-roller trait.*

4. Have your partner use Figure 19.6 to determine your type of hairline. Widow's peak (W) is dominant over no widow's peak (w).

Widow's peak

No widow's peak

Figure 19.6 *Which kind of hairline do you have?*

5. Record on both chromosomes, just below the tongue-roller genes, the symbols for the genes that reflect your type of hairline.

6. The ability to detect a bitter taste in taster paper is dominant (T) over the lack of such ability (t). Obtain two pieces of taster paper from your teacher. Put one on your tongue and mix it with your saliva for about 15 seconds. Dispose of it and do the same with the second piece of paper. If you detect a bitter taste when you chew either of the pieces of paper, you express the taster trait. If you do not detect a bitter taste from either piece of paper, you do not express that trait. Record the symbols for the genes that reflect your taste ability just below the symbols for your type of hairline.

7. Figure 19.7 illustrates the differences between hanging and attached ear lobes. Hanging ear lobes (H) are dominant over attached ear lobes (h). Have your partner determine how your ears are attached. Record in the last space on your chromosomes the symbols for the genes that determine your type of earlobe.

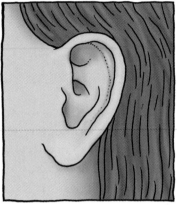

Hanging earlobes

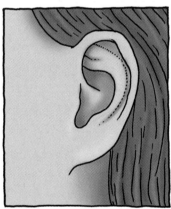

Attached earlobes

Figure 19.7 *Have your partner identify your type of earlobe.*

8. Toward the end of interphase, each chromosome in a future sex cell duplicates—that is, makes an exact copy of itself. To represent this process, you should now copy the appropriate trait symbols onto each duplicated chromosome shown on the student sheets.

9. At the bottom right of your student sheet, notice that a single chromosome from each pair has moved into a separate sex cell—sperm cells on Student Sheet 19.2A and egg cells on the front and back of Student Sheet 19.2B. These cells are numbered 1–4. Label each chromosome with the appropriate symbols for the four traits.

10. Use the spinner (shown in figure 19.9) to decide which chromosome—1, 2, 3, or 4—will pair with a chromosome from the opposite sex.

11. The pair in each group with Student Sheet 19.2A should use scissors to cut out the numbered chromosome identified by the spinner. The other pair in the group should tape it next to the spinner-selected chromosome in the egg on the back of Student Sheet 19.2B. This simulates the fertilization process. Note that although the male and female chromosomes are drawn to scale, the sperm and eggs are not. Figure 19.8 shows the relative sizes of egg and sperm cells.

12. Examine the gene pair for each trait in the fertilized egg. List the genotype and phenotype for each trait next to the fertilized egg. Discuss with your partner which traits of the newly formed offspring differ from those of the male parent, the female parent, and from those of both parents.

13. Follow your teacher's instructions for cleanup.

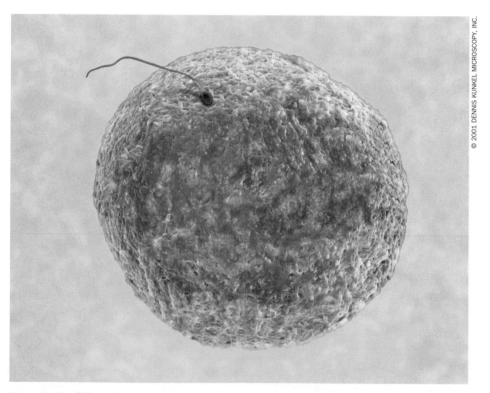

Figure 19.8 *Although the sperm and egg on your student sheets are shown to be the same size, an egg is considerably larger than a sperm, as you can see in this photo.*

Inquiry 19.3
Introducing Clyde and Claire

PROCEDURE

1. Decide which pair in your group will create a cartoon character named Clyde and which will create a cartoon character named Claire.

2. Notice on Student Sheet 19.3A that the round head gene (R) is dominant over the block head gene (r). This trait and the trait for nose width are the only two that have been created specifically for this inquiry. The others are legitimate human traits. Use the spinner to see whether your cartoon character will be homozygous round headed, heterozygous round headed, or homozygous block headed for head shape. Record the genotype and resulting phenotype on the student sheet.

3. Use the spinner to determine the genotypes for the rest of your character's traits. Each trait requires a separate spin.

4. With your partner, agree on the phenotype that results from each genotype. Print each phenotype in the appropriate space on the student sheet.

5. Begin drawing your character's head, as determined by its phenotype, about 7 cm from the top of a sheet of unlined paper. Do your initial drawing lightly in pencil to allow for revisions later.

6. Next, draw the outline of your character's hair and hairline, making it appropriate for your character's gender—male or female.

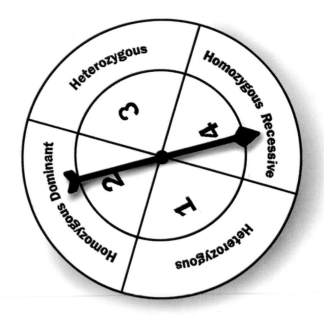

Figure 19.9 *The condition selected by the arrow on this spinner is homozygous recessive. As a result, the phenotype for head shape is rr or block headed.*

7. Continue drawing each of your character's facial traits lightly in pencil until your drawing is complete. Make sure that the phenotype of each trait expresses the genotype determined by the spinner.

8. When you have drawn all the traits lightly in pencil, get approval from your teacher to retrace them with a black fineline marker. Add hair and eye color last with your colored pencils. Use black or brown pencils for dark eyes and green or blue pencils for light-colored eyes. Use black or brown pencils for dark hair and a yellow pencil for light (blonde) hair.

9. Print the symbols for each genotype next to the appropriate trait on the drawing.

10. Share your character's genotypes and phenotypes with those of the other pair in your group. Record the other pair's information in the appropriate columns on Student Sheet 19.3A.

11. Working with your partner, complete the Punnett squares on Student Sheet 19.3B to determine the possible genotypes that Clyde's and Claire's offspring could have for each trait, beginning with head shape. Then use the spinner to determine which of these genotypes the offspring actually inherits. Record your information on Student Sheet 19.3A and 19.3B.

12. Determine the sex of the offspring. The chromosome pair that represents a female is XX; a male, XY. They are referred to in this manner because the chromosomes, when seen under high magnification, are actually shaped like those letters. The gene that determines maleness is only on the "Y" chromosome. Complete a Punnett square using the chromosome letters X and Y rather than gene symbols. Then use the spinner to decide the sex of the offspring. Record the results on your student sheets.

13. Now draw the offspring using the same procedure you used to draw your parent. Be sure all of the features reflect the phenotypes you listed on Student Sheet 19.3A.

14. Be prepared to share your Clyde and Claire and their offspring with the class. Include in your presentation how many of the eight traits displayed by the offspring also were—

- displayed by Clyde
- displayed by Claire
- displayed by both parents
- displayed by neither parent

Also be prepared to give your interpretation of why the offspring displayed traits not observed in either parent.

REFLECTING ON WHAT YOU'VE DONE

On the basis of what you have learned in this lesson, respond to the following in your science notebook.

A. Which determines the other—phenotype or genotype? Explain.

B. In pea plants, the gene for purple "P" flowers is dominant over the gene for white "p" flowers.

- What is the genotype of a heterozygous purple-flowered pea plant?
- What is the genotype of a white-flowered pea plant?

C. How is the product of meiosis different from that of mitosis?

D. A squirrel normally has 40 pairs of chromosomes in its cells.

- After mitosis occurs, how many pairs of chromosomes would be in each of the squirrel's body cells?
- After meiosis occurs, how many pairs of chromosomes would be in each of its sex cells?

E. How would you respond to a student who says, "Because the offspring develops inside the female, it will be more like her"?

F. During Inquiry 19.3, you may have noticed that some offspring displayed more traits like those of their fathers and some displayed more traits like those of their mothers. If each parent donates one gene for each trait, how can this happen?

G. Hanging earlobes (H) are dominant over attached earlobes (h). Complete a Punnett square showing the possible offspring from an Hh male and an hh female. Then answer the following questions:

• What are the chances of these parents having an offspring with hanging earlobes?
• If these parents have four offspring, will two definitely have hanging earlobes and two definitely have attached earlobes? Explain.
• If an offspring has attached earlobes, can we assume its genotype is hh? Explain.
• If an offspring has hanging earlobes, can we assume its genotype is Hh? Explain.

H. Occasionally a trait that was not observed in either parent appears in an offspring. Explain how this can happen.

I. Which parent actually determines the sex of an offspring? Explain.

J. Each time the spinner was used in Inquiry 19.3, Clyde or Claire had the potential to be homozygous dominant, heterozygous, or homozygous recessive for a trait. What must be true about the genotypes of both of their parents for each trait?

K. Look again at the photo of genetic corn on the first page of this lesson. Explain why there are two colors of seeds on the same ear of corn. Also explain which color is dominant and why.

Mendel's Discoveries

Gregor Mendel

As you begin your study of heredity, you may be feeling like many scientists did until a man named Gregor Mendel came along. Mendel was born in 1822 and spent most of his adult life as a monk in Austria. Mendel's studies of garden peas started to lift the cloud of confusion about how traits are passed on from one generation to the next.

At first, Mendel was bewildered by the behavior of certain traits of pea plants. For example, when he grew pea plants from seeds produced by certain tall pea plants that he had pollinated with pollen from short pea plants, Mendel expected all of the offspring to be of medium height. Instead, all of the offspring were tall. Every time he repeated this procedure with the same plants, he got the same results. It seemed that there was something about the tall trait that overwhelmed, or dominated, the short trait. Mendel called this stronger trait the "dominant trait." He called the trait that was dominated the "recessive trait," because it seemed to recede, or vanish.

These pea plants display the ideal ratio of tall to short plants for offspring of parents that each had a dominant and recessive gene for height.

Mendel then decided to try something different. He took a group of the tall offspring and cross pollinated them, using a process similar to the one you used to cross pollinate your Fast Plants. He harvested the seeds and replanted them. Surprisingly, he found some short pea plants among the offspring. Mendel detected a pattern to his results that helped him to recognize some of the fundamental principles of heredity.

Mendel was convinced that the male and the female pea plant each contributed something during fertilization that helped determine a trait. Since each parent contributed something, he concluded there had to be a pair of these "somethings" that determined, for example, whether the plant would be tall or short. We now know that these "somethings" are genes. The traits that Mendel observed in pea plants are each determined by a pair of genes—one gene from the male and one from the female.

Mendel used an upper case letter to represent the dominant gene. For example, he used "T" as the symbol for the tallness gene in pea plants. He used a lower case "t" as the symbol for shortness in pea plants. Mendel believed that whenever an organism expresses, or displays, a dominant trait, at least one dominant gene must be present. For example, if a pea plant is tall, its gene pair has to be either "TT" or "Tt." Table 19.1: Mendel's Study of Traits in Pea Plants describes the dominant and recessive forms of seven traits of pea plants that Mendel studied. It also shows the number of offspring from Mendel's research that express the dominant or recessive form of each trait. Each results from a cross between two parents that had one dominant and one recessive gene for the trait—Tt × Tt, for example. ☐

Table 19.1 Mendel's Study of Traits in Pea Plants

Trait	Illustration of Trait	Offspring Expressing Dominant Trait	Offspring Expressing Recessive Trait	Total Number of Offspring
Plant height		787 tall (T)	277 short (t)	1064
Flower position		651 axial flowers along stem (A)	207 terminal flowers at the tip of stems (a)	858
Flower color		705 purple flowers (P)	224 white flowers (p)	929
Pod shape		882 smooth pods (S)	299 bumpy pods (s)	1181

Table 19.1 Mendel's Study of Traits in Pea Plants (continued)

Trait	Illustration of Trait	Offspring Expressing Dominant Trait	Offspring Expressing Recessive Trait	Total Number of Offspring
Pod color		428 green pods (G)	152 yellow pods (g)	580
Seed shape		5474 round seeds (R)	1850 wrinkled seeds (r)	7324
Seed color		6002 yellow seeds (Y)	2001 green seeds (y)	8003

What Are the Chances?

Reginald Punnett

Early in the 20th century, an English geneticist at Cambridge University developed a tool to display the possible ways that genes could pair during a genetic cross. His name was Reginald Punnett, and the tool came to be known as the "Punnett square."

Punnett used the square to illustrate the probability of the outcomes that could result from a cross, or mating, between two parents, primarily in sweet peas. The simplest Punnett square consists of a large box divided into four small boxes. To use it, you would write the genes for a trait from one parent (usually the female) above the square, and the genes for the same trait from the male on the left side of the square. Because only one chromosome from each pair passes into an offspring's sex cell during sexual reproduction, each egg above the square would contain only one gene from the female's genotype, while each sperm to the left of the square would contain only one gene from the male's genotype. Inside the square itself, you would write the possible outcomes.

As an example, a brown-eyed male could have the genotype "Bb" for eye color. A blue-eyed female could have the genotype "bb." To use a Punnett square to illustrate a cross between these parents, you would take each gene for eye color from the male and show how it could combine with each gene for eye color from the female. The shortcut for writing the cross between these parents would be "Bb × bb."

A Punnett square does not predict which genes actually will become part of the offspring's

genotype. It only shows the probability that specific genotypes will occur. In this illustration, only one trait is shown in each sperm and egg. However, most organisms pass on thousands of traits during fertilization. ☐

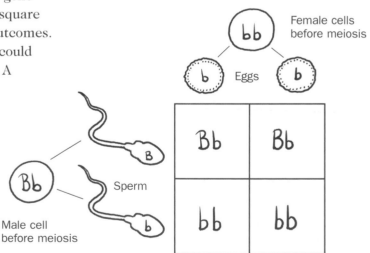

This example of a completed Punnett square shows the possible genotypes from a cross between a brown-eyed male with the genotype "Bb" and a blue-eyed female with the genotype "bb."

Hello, Dolly!

Although Dolly looked like any other white Finn Dorset, genetically she was very special.

To us, she might have looked just like any other sheep of her species on the green hills of Scotland. But this sheep, named Dolly and born in March 1997, was special. Dolly was the first animal to be created by a process called "cloning."

Instead of having two biological parents, Dolly was created from the DNA of just one parent—a six-year-old female sheep, or ewe. This meant that Dolly had the same genes as the ewe, a species of white sheep called a Finn Dorset. She was a genetic copy—a clone—of the ewe. News of Dolly's birth rocked the world.

The Usual Way

During normal reproduction in mammals, a male sperm and a female egg unite at the moment of fertilization and a new cell, called a "zygote," forms. The zygote contains DNA from both the male and female. The number of chromosome pairs varies with the species; for example, a human zygote receives 23 single chromosomes from each parent, giving it a total of 23 pairs.

The zygote begins to divide and grow and in time—about nine months for a human and about five months for a sheep—a baby is born.

The DNA received from both parents will determine its skin, hair, and eye colors, along with many other traits.

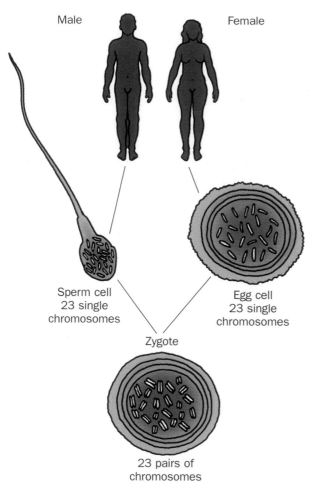

Each parent contributes an equal number of chromosomes to the offspring.

The Cloning Way

Dolly did not come about in the "usual way." To create Dolly, scientists first removed the nucleus from an egg cell of a Scottish Blackface sheep. The nucleus of a cell contains its DNA. Without its nucleus, a cell is sort of like a head without a brain.

But scientists didn't leave the egg cell without a nucleus for long. Into it, they put a nucleus from a body cell of the Finn Dorset. This nucleus, like the nucleus of a body cell of every mammal, contained a complete set of

chromosome pairs needed for new life. Scientists zapped the egg cell with a tiny charge of electricity to stimulate the custom-made zygote to begin dividing.

The zygote was then implanted into the reproductive organ of the Scottish Blackface ewe. Dolly was born 148 days later. She was all white, just like her genetic mother. Scientists knew immediately that she was a clone. Why? Because Scottish Blackface sheep do not normally produce all-white offspring.

As you can see, Dolly and her surrogate mother are quite different in appearance.

Clones and Twins

Genetically, being a clone is like being an identical twin. Identical twins, like clones, form from a single zygote. So identical twins have identical genes. Yet they often grow up to be very different from each other. That's because we—people *and* other animals—are more than just our genes. Our external environment, our upbringing, our experiences, and even the food we eat all influence who we become.

Fraternal twins form from simultaneous fertilization of two different eggs by two different sperm; therefore, they are no more alike genetically than siblings conceived at different times.

The Future of Cloning
Successful cloning of sheep didn't happen overnight. In fact, scientists had tried unsuccessfully to clone sheep 276 times before Dolly was born.

The process is complicated and expensive, and many things can go wrong. Several sheep, as well as pigs, mice, and other animals, have been cloned since Dolly. Most have serious problems with their hearts, livers, and immune systems.

So, what about cloning humans? A few scientists think they have the expertise to do it. But many people think this is a very bad idea. What do you think? ☐

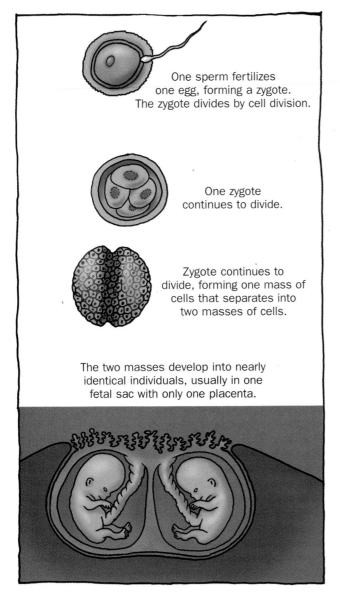 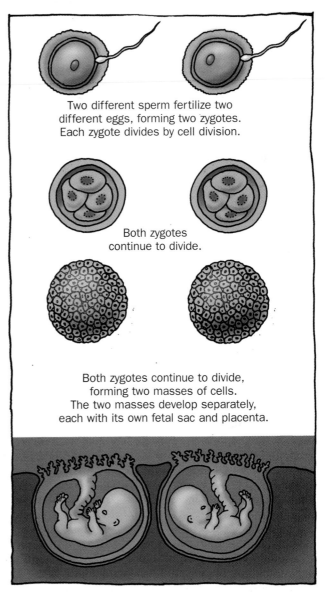

Identical twins (on the left) develop when a zygote divides once and each daughter cell forms an identical human being. Fraternal twins (on the right) develop when two sperm fertilize two separate eggs.

The Key to Organisms— An Assessment

There are many different species of fruits and vegetables shown here. How could you develop a key with which to identify each species if the others were not present?

KEITH WELLER, AGRICULTURAL RESEARCH SERVICE/UNITED STATES DEPARTMENT OF AGRICULTURE

INTRODUCTION

In this lesson, you will use what you have learned about the organisms on the organism photo cards to create two kinds of dichotomous keys for identifying those organisms. Your teacher will introduce you to dichotomous keys during "Getting Started." You will practice constructing written dichotomous keys that identify some of your classmates and various organisms. Then you will create, on a piece of poster paper, a graphical dichotomous key for 13 of the organisms on the photo cards. From this graphical key, you will prepare a written key and attach it to the poster.

OBJECTIVES FOR THIS LESSON

Develop written dichotomous keys for various organisms pictured on Student Sheets.

Create a graphical dichotomous key for 13 of the organisms on the organism photo cards.

Develop a written dichotomous key from the graphical dichotomous key.

Getting Started

Listen and participate as your teacher guides you through an activity that introduces you to the concept of a dichotomous key.

MATERIALS FOR LESSON 20

For each student
- 2 copies of Student Sheet 20.1A: Dichotomous Key Template

For your group
- 2 copies of Student Sheet 20.1B: Organism Sets
- 1 copy of Student Sheet 20.2: Dichotomous Key Template for Organisms
- 1 set of organism photo cards
- 1 sheet of poster board or construction paper
- 1 black marker
- 1 metric ruler, 30 cm (12 in.) Transparent tape

Glossary

abdomen: A segment of the body of many animals. The abdomen is the third body segment of insects. *See also* **thorax.**

abiotic: Having to do with nonliving things.

adaptation (genetic): Any change in the structure of an organism that affects its ability to survive and reproduce in a particular environment and that may be passed to the organism's offspring through its genes.

allele: One of the different forms of the same gene for a particular trait.

anaphase: Stage of mitosis and meiosis when chromosomes migrate toward the poles.

antennae: Appendages of an insect's head used for smelling and touching.

asexual reproduction: The process by which new organisms are formed from a single parent without the union of male and female sex cells. The new organisms are genetically identical to the parent.

bacteria: Tiny, unicellular organisms that lack a defined nucleus and belong to the kingdom Monera.

biology: The study of things that are or were once living.

biotic: Having to do with living things.

budding: A form of asexual reproduction during which an outgrowth of an organism, formed through cell division, breaks off and becomes an independent organism.

carnivore: Any flesh-eating organism.

castings: Solid wastes released by earthworms.

caterpillar: The larval stage of a butterfly or moth.

cell: The smallest organized unit of living protoplasm.

cell division: The process by which cells increase in number. *See also* **mitosis; cytokinesis.**

cell membrane: The outermost living layer of plant and animal cells that regulates what enters and leaves the cell.

cell wall: The outermost, rigid, nonliving layer of plant cells.

cellular respiration: The process by which glucose combines with oxygen to produce energy, carbon dioxide, and water.

chromatid: One of a pair of duplicated chromosomes, joined at their middle by a centromere.

chromatin: A mass of elongated deoxyribonucleic acid (DNA). *See also* **DNA; chromosome.**

chromosome: A body composed of DNA, which can be seen in a nucleus during mitosis. *See also* **DNA.**

chrysalis: The pupal stage of butterflies and moths during which larval structures are broken down and adult structures are formed.

cilia (singular: cilium): Tiny, hair-like extensions of cells that aid in movement.

climax community: A relatively stable community of organisms that results from ecological succession.

clitellum: A saddle-like structure, which surrounds part of an earthworm and produces mucus, which forms a sheath around mating earthworms and a cocoon around their eggs.

cloning: The process of producing an offspring that is genetically identical to its parent.

community: All of the living things in an area.

compound light microscope: A microscope that uses two lenses and light to make a specimen visible.

cotyledon: The first leaf or one of a pair of leaves developed by the embryo within a seed.

coverslip: A piece of glass or clear plastic that is placed over the specimen on a microscope slide.

cutting: A twig or branch that is cut from one plant and used to grow another, separate plant; one way in which asexual reproduction occurs in plants.

cyst: A tough, protective envelope that forms around certain microorganisms.

cytokinesis: The splitting of one cell into two. *See also* cell division; mitosis.

cytoplasm: The living material within the cell membrane.

decomposition: The breaking down of a substance into simpler substances.

deoxyribonucleic acid (DNA): Hereditary material of which chromosomes are comprised. *See also* **chromosome.**

depression slide: A microscope slide that has a concave area in which to put a drop of liquid or a specimen.

dichotomous key: Pairs of opposing questions or statements about observable traits that eventually lead to the identity of an object or organism.

dicotyledon: A plant whose seed contains two seed leaves.

digestion: The breakdown of food into simpler particles that can be used as nutrients by an organism.

diploid: A term that refers to the normal number of paired chromosomes in a body cell of an organism.

dominant: A gene that controls its recessive form and determines the phenotype.

dormancy: A period during which organisms reduce their level of activity to a minimum to survive unfavorable environmental conditions.

dry-mount slide: A microscope slide on which no water is used.

ecosystem: A community of organisms interacting with their abiotic environment.

embryo: The stage of an organism that follows fertilization and continues until hatching or germination.

evolution: A theory that states that organisms have descended from earlier forms and involves changes in organisms' genetic makeup, which are passed on through many generations.

excretion: The process by which animals eliminate waste products.

exoskeleton: A hard outer shell that covers the bodies of certain animals, including crustaceans and insects.

fermentation: A type of cellular respiration that occurs in plants and does not require oxygen.

fertilization: The union of sperm (male) and egg (female).

fertilizer: A substance composed of a mixture of nutrient substances in proportions necessary for plant growth.

field of view: The maximum area that is visible through the lens of a microscope.

flagellum (plural: flagella): Whip-like extension of a cell that aids in movement.

focus: To adjust the position of a lens in order to make a clear image.

fragmentation: A form of asexual reproduction in which a piece of an organism breaks off and regenerates into a new organism.

frass: Solid wastes excreted by insect larvae.

frond: The leaves of aquatic plants such as *Lemna.*

gene: One of many portions of a DNA molecule that contains genetic instructions.

generation: A group of organisms that are from the same parents.

genetics: The study of heredity.

genotype: The gene makeup for a trait.

genus (plural: genera): A category of biological classification that ranks between family and species; always the first part of a scientific name; written in Latin or Greek.

germination: The beginning of growth or sprouting of a seed.

graft: The transfer of one plant part, such as a twig, to the rooting portion, or stock, of another plant.

guard cell: One of a pair of specialized leaf epidermal cells that work together to control the formation of stomata. *See* **stomata.**

habitat: The place where an organism naturally lives.

haploid: A term that refers to the number of unpaired chromosomes in a sex cell of an organism.

herbivore: Any plant-eating organism.

heredity: The passing of traits from parents to offspring.

heterozygous: A condition in which the paired genes for a trait are different; often referred to as hybrid.

homozygous: A condition in which the paired genes for a trait are the same.

invertebrate: An animal without a backbone.

larva: The pre-adult form of many organisms, such as butterflies and moths.

leaf: The photosynthetic organ of the plant that includes a petiole (stem), blade, and veins.

lens: A piece of curved glass or other clear material that bends light rays. Lenses can help make things look clearer, larger, and closer.

life cycle: The stages an organism goes through from conception through death.

life process: One of many processes, such as respiration, digestion, or reproduction, required for an organism to survive.

meiosis: A reproductive process in which the nucleus divides and four haploid sex cells form.

metamorphosis: A striking change in form or structure of the body of some animals, especially insects, as they proceed through their life cycle.

metaphase: Stage of mitosis and meiosis in which the chromosomes line up in the middle of the cell.

microorganism: An organism that cannot be seen without magnification.

mitosis: The process consisting of four phases during which the nucleus divides, and two genetically identical nuclei result.

molt: To shed feathers, hair, or skin.

monocotyledon: A plant whose seed contains one seed leaf.

mycelium: The vegetative body of a fungus.

nectar: A sweet liquid produced by flowers, the aroma of which attracts insects and birds.

nematocyst: Poisonous threads in the sting cells of certain organisms, such as *Hydra* and jellyfish.

nitrogen (N): A nutrient needed by plants to promote the growth of leaves and overall plant health. *See also* **phosphorus; potassium.**

nucleus: The "command center" of the cell; regulates cell functions and contains the DNA.

nutrient: A substance that an organism takes in and uses for growth and development.

objective lenses: Lenses of different magnifications on a microscope.

offspring: A new organism that results from asexual or sexual reproduction.

omnivore: An organism that eats both flesh and plant matter. *See also* **carnivore; herbivore.**

organ: A group of tissues working together to perform a specific function.

organelle: One of many structures in a cell that performs a specific function.

organism: A living creature.

osmosis: The diffusion of water through a selectively permeable membrane.

ovule (egg): A female reproductive cell.

phenotype: The physical expression of a trait as a result of its genotype.

phosphorus (P): A nutrient needed by plants to promote strong, healthy roots and flower blooming. *See also* **nitrogen; potassium.**

photoreceptor: A structure or pigment sensitive to light.

photosynthesis: The process by which chlorophyll-containing cells use energy from the Sun to combine water and carbon dioxide to produce glucose and to release oxygen as a byproduct.

pistil: The female reproductive organ of flowering plants.

pollen grain: The male reproductive cell of flowering plants.

pollination: The transfer of pollen from an anther to a stigma in the same flower or in a different flower of the same species.

population: A group of individuals of a species occupying a specific region.

potassium (K): An essential nutrient needed by plants to enable them to withstand dramatic temperature changes and to help protect them from disease. *See also* **nitrogen; phosphorus.**

proboscis: The elongated sucking mouth part of certain insects, such as butterflies.

prophase: Stage of mitosis and meiosis in which chromosomes become visible.

protist: A group of one-celled organisms with well-defined nuclei, which belong in the kingdom Protista.

protoplasm: A general term for the living material within a cell.

pseudopod: The "false foot" of protists such as an amoeba, which is composed of flowing cytoplasm. In amoebae, they aid in movement and in capturing food.

Punnett square: A chart used to display the potential genotypes of offspring from a particular male and female parent.

recessive: A gene that can be controlled by a dominant form; only expressed phenotypically when both genes in a pair are recessive.

regeneration: The process by which certain organisms produce new body parts.

reproduction: The process of creating organisms of the same species.

root hair: An outgrowth of an epidermal cell of a root that increases its surface, or absorptive, area.

runner: An extension of a plant stem, which runs over the ground as it grows, touches down, takes root, and develops another plant at that location. Certain plants reproduce asexually by producing runners.

scanning electron microscope (SEM): An instrument that bounces electrons off objects to create a three-dimensional image that is more highly magnified than possible through a light microscope.

scientific name: A universally used name for an organism; consists of two words representing the organism's genus and species. Scientific names are derived from Latin or Greek terms.

seed leaf: *See* **cotyledon.**

seed pod: A fruit, often dry, that contains seeds.

segment: A body section of an organism.

setae: Tiny, hair-like structures on the body of certain annelids, such as earthworms, that help them grip a surface.

species: The last part of a scientific name, ranked after genus in biological classification; also applies to a group of interbreeding organisms that share similar characteristics.

spore: A sexual or asexual reproductive cell of an organism.

stamen: The male reproductive organ of flowering plants.

stoma (plural: stomata): The opening in the surface of a leaf through which water vapor and gasses pass.

succession: A series of progressive changes in the plant and animal life in an area that leads to a climax community in which the numbers and types of organisms are in relative balance.

surface area: The area of an object, such as a root hair, that is in direct contact with its environment.

symbiotic: A term that describes a relationship between two organisms in which both organisms benefit.

taxonomy: The science of classifying living things.

telophase: Stage of mitosis and meiosis, just prior to cytokinesis, where individual chromosomes are not visible.

thorax: In insects, the body part between the head and abdomen. *See also* **abdomen.**

tissue: A group of cells working together to perform a specific function.

trait: An inherited characteristic of an organism.

transpiration: The process by which water passes from the inside of a leaf to the atmosphere.

variable: A factor in an experiment that can be changed and measured.

vertebrate: An animal with a backbone. *See also* **invertebrate.**

wet-mount slide: Two microscope slides, or a slide and coverslip, with a drop of liquid and/or a specimen between them.

Index

Photo Credits

Part 1: The Beginning xviii–1 Eric Long, Smithsonian Institution 3 Eric Long, Smithsonian Institution 6 Dr. Barry Meyers-Rice, Galleria Carnivora 8 (left) Dwight R. Kuhn (right) © Charles O' Rear/Corbis (bottom) © Joe McDonald/Corbis 9 Courtesy of the Hunt Institute for Botanical Documentation, Carnegie Mellon University, Pittsburgh, Pennsylvania 11 (top) Fire Ant Project, Texas A & M University (bottom) Courtesy Entomology Department, Smithsonian Institution, Washington, D.C. 12 Courtesy of Henry Milne/ © NSRC 22 Chip Clark, National Museum of Natural History, Smithsonian Institution 23 (top) Cirad-Prifas, France (bottom) Marlin E. Rice, Professor of Entomology, Iowa State University 24 (top) Courtesy of R.W. Matthews (bottom) Courtesy of Carolina Biological Supply Company 26 Courtesy of The Library of Congress 27 (top left) By permission of the President and Council of the Royal Society, London (top right) Historical Collections, National Museum of Health & Medicine, Armed Forces Institute of Pathology, Washington D.C. (bottom) Eric Erbe, Agricultural Research Service/United States Department of Agriculture 28 Dwight R. Kuhn 30 Courtesy of Henry Milne/© NSRC 31 Courtesy of Henry Milne/ © NSRC 32 Courtesy of Henry Milne/© NSRC 35 (top left and right) William R. West/Carolina Biological Supply Company (bottom) Courtesy of Carolina Biological Supply Company 36 (both) Courtesy of Carolina Biological Supply Company 37 Dwight R. Kuhn 38 © 2000 National Gallery of Art, Washington, D.C. 43 Courtesy of Henry Milne/© NSRC 44 (top) Courtesy of Carolina Biological Supply Company (bottom) Animals Animals © McDonald Wildlife Photography 45 National Oceanic and Atmospheric Administration (NOAA) Photo Library/NOAA Central Library 46 Keith Weller, Agricultural Research Service/United States Department of Agriculture 47 Smithsonian Institution, Horticulture Services Division, Archives of American Gardens 49 (all) Courtesy Potash & Phosphate Institute, Norcross, Georgia 56 Courtesy of Wisconsin Fast Plants 57 Courtesy of Wisconsin Fast Plants 58 (top) National Aeronautics and Space Administration (bottom) Courtesy of Mary Musgrave 61 © 1998 Willy A. Verheulpen 64 Courtesy of Wisconsin Fast Plants 66 Courtesy of Wisconsin Fast Plants 67 Courtesy of Carolina Biological Supply Company 71 Courtesy of Henry Milne/© NSRC 72 Courtesy of Wisconsin Fast Plants 73 Courtesy of Wisconsin Fast Plants 74 (all) Courtesy of Carolina Biological Supply Company 75 Courtesy of Wisconsin Fast Plants 76 Courtesy of Carolina Biological Supply Company 77 Courtesy of Carolina Biological Supply Company 78 Jessie Cohen, Smithsonian National Zoo 79 (top) Smithsonian Institution (bottom) United States Geological Survey, Gordon Rodda 80 (both) Agricultural Research Service/United States Department of Agriculture 81 (top) Scott Bauer, Agricultural Research Service/United States Department of Agriculture (middle) United States Department of Agriculture/Forest Service (bottom) Courtesy of Carolina Biological Supply Company 82 Courtesy of Carolina Biological Supply Company 87 Courtesy of Carolina Biological Supply Company 91 Courtesy of Carolina Biological Supply Company 92 (both) Courtesy of Carolina Biological Supply Company

Part 2: Continuing the Cycle 94–95 Courtesy of Henry Milne/© NSRC 96 © Dennis Kunkel Microscopy, Inc. 99 All Photos Courtesy of Carolina Biological Supply Company 100 All Photos Courtesy of Carolina Biological Supply Company 102 Courtesy of Carolina Biological Supply Company 106 Corbis/ Royalty-Free 107 Courtesy of Henry Milne/© NSRC 109 Courtesy of Carolina Biological Supply Company 110 Courtesy of Henry Milne/© NSRC 113 All Photos Courtesy of Carolina Biological Supply Company 117 Dwight R. Kuhn 118 Courtesy of Carolina Biological Supply Company 119 Top Photos Courtesy of Carolina Biological Supply Company (bottom) Smithsonian Institution, Archives of American Gardens, Mary Livingston Ripley Center 120 © Joel Sartore/Corbis

122 Courtesy of Carolina Biological Supply Company
125 Courtesy of Henry Milne/© NSRC 126 Courtesy
of Carolina Biological Supply Company 127 Courtesy
of Carolina Biological Supply Company 132 Dwight R.
Kuhn 136 Courtesy of Henry Milne/© NSRC 138
Courtesy of Henry Milne/© NSRC 141 Both Photos
Courtesy of Carolina Biological Supply Company
142 Milos Kalab 143 Jed Kirschbaum, The Baltimore
Sun 145 Dwight R. Kuhn 146 Stephen G. Maka Pho-
tography 148 Courtesy of Carolina Biological Supply
Company 149 (both) Courtesy of Carolina Biological
Supply Company 150 (both) © Wayne P. Armstrong
152–153 Michael P. Gadomski/The National Audobon
Society Collection/Photo Researchers, Inc.

Part 3: Completing the Cycle 156–157 Eric Long,
Smithsonian Institution 158 (both) Courtesy of Carolina Biological Supply Company 160 (both) Cour-
tesy of Carolina Biological Supply Company 161 (all)
Courtesy of Carolina Biological Supply Company
163 © 2001 Robert Houser 165 English Heritage
166 Charledonezan 167 (both) Dwight R. Kuhn
169 Dwight R. Kuhn 170 (both) Courtesy of Carolina
Biological Supply Company 171 Corbis/Royalty-Free
172 © Brian Kuhn/Dwight Kuhn Photography 173
Dwight R. Kuhn 174 Courtesy of Carolina Biological
Supply Company 175 Courtesy of Carolina Biological
Supply Company 176 Courtesy of Carolina Biological
Supply Company 177 (top) Dwight R. Kuhn (bottom)
Courtesy of Carolina Biological Supply Company
179 (top) Dwight R. Kuhn (bottom) Keith Weller, Agri-
cultural Research Service/United States Department of
Agriculture 180 Jacqueline Ramseyer, Willow Glen
Resident 182 Library of Congress, Prints & Pho-
tographs Division, LC-USZ62-3499 186 T.K Maugel,
Laboratory for Biological Ultrastructure, University of
Maryland, College Park 187 (top) © AFP/Corbis
(center) Scott Bauer, Agricultural Research Service/
United States Department of Agriculture (bottom)
Northwind Picture Archives 188 Dwight R. Kuhn
189 (both) Courtesy of Carolina Biological Supply
Company 190 Courtesy of Carolina Biological Supply

Company 193 Wim Van Egmond 194 Dwight R.
Kuhn 201 Courtesy of Carolina Biological Supply
Company 202 Courtesy "All Stings Considered" by
Craig Thomas, M.D., and Susan Scott 203 © Steve
Kaufman/Corbis 204 Dwight R. Kuhn 205 © Wayne
P. Armstrong 2000 209 © 1999 Dai Crisp 210 Bob
Nichols, Agricultural Research Service/United States
Department of Agriculture 211 Hunt Institute for
Botanical Documentation, Carnegie Mellon University,
Pittsburgh, Pennsylvania 212 (both) Courtesy of
Wisconsin Fast Plants 214 (both) Courtesy of Wis-
consin Fast Plants 215 Courtesy of Wisconsin Fast
Plants 216 Courtesy of Carolina Biological Supply
Company 218 (top) Animals Animals © Dominique
Braud (bottom) Animals Animals © Sunset/Brake
219 Courtesy of Carolina Biological Supply Company
222 © 2001 Dennis Kunkel Microscopy, Inc. 226
National Library of Medicine, National Institutes of
Health 232 Reproduced by Permission of The Master
and Fellows of Gonville and Caius College, Cambridge
233 Courtesy of Roslin Institute, Scotland 234 Courtesy of Roslin Institute, Scotland 236 Keith Weller,
Agricultural Research Service/United States Department of Agriculture 241 Courtesy of Peg Koetch
242 Courtesy of Peg Koetch